Version 1.2 – published May 4th 2022

This document was initially launched on March 1st 2022 as a consultation draft while still formally in development. A final version was published on April 27th following revisions in response to feedback. Further changes may take place so please **check you are reading the most up-to-date version** at https://www.themindfulnessinitiative.org/reconnection

Acknowledgments

Contributors: Daniel Fischer (Wageningen University), Chris Ives (University of Nottingham), Ruth Ormston (Mindfulness Initiative), Lena Ramstetter (University of Salzburg), Ute Thiermann (Imperial College London), and Sophie Sansom (Bangor University)

Additional thanks for research input to Pascal Frank (Stanford University), Sonja Geiger (Justus Liebig University) and Ulf Schrader (Technische Universität Berlin)

Reviewers: Nadine Andrews (Scottish Government), Thomas Bruhn (Institute for Advanced Sustainability Studies, Potsdam), Jane Chun (Compassion Institute), Rebecca Crane (Bangor University), Alex Evans (A Larger Us), James Gimian (Foundation for a Mindful Society), Philippe Goldin (University of California, Davis), Daniel Gortz (Metamoderna), Heather Grabbe (Open Society European Policy Institute), Matt Hawkins (Compassion in Politics), Felicia Huppert (University of Cambridge), Ruth Layton (Sankalpa), Mark Leonard (Mindfulness Connected), Jeremy Lent (Deep Transformation Network), Jürgen Nagller (Wellbeing Mindset Initiative), Dan Nixon (Perspectiva), Karen Neil (Institute of Health Promotion and Education), Kate Pumphrey (A Larger Us), Dan Siegel (UCLA School of Medicine), Laureline Simon (One Resilient Earth), David Tyfield (Lancaster University), Katherine Weare (University of Southampton) and Katie White (WWF).

Funding: This project was supported by the Emergence Foundation. The work of the Mindfulness Initiative is supported by the Lostand Foundation, Sankalpa and the Mindful Trust.

Research for this report was also supported by two projects funded by the Swedish Research Council Formas: i) Mind4Change (grant number 2019-00390; full title: Agents of Change: Mind, Cognitive Bias and Decision-Making in a Context of Social and Climate Change), and ii) TransVision (grant number 2019-01969; full title: Transition Visions: Coupling Society, Well-being and Energy Systems for Transitioning to a Fossil-free Society).

EMERGENCE FOUNDATION

Copyright © 2022 The Mindfulness Initiative

Sheffield, S1, United Kingdom

The Mindfulness Initiative is a Charitable Incorporated Organisation, registered number: 1179834 (England & Wales)

Writing: Jamie Bristow, Rosie Bell & Christine Wamsler
Research: Jamie Bristow & Christine Wamsler

Illustrations by Ben the Illustrator: https://bentheillustrator.com/
Report design by J-P Stanway

This report should be cited as:
Bristow, J., Bell, R., Wamsler, C. (2022). Reconnection: Meeting the Climate Crisis Inside Out. Research and policy report. The Mindfulness Initiative and LUCSUS. www.themindfulnessinitiative.org/reconnection

ISBN 978-1-913353-06-3

 This work is licensed under a Creative Commons Attribution-NonCommercial-NoDerivatives 4.0 International License.

About the Authors

Jamie Bristow

Jamie Bristow is Co-Director of The Mindfulness Initiative. After supporting UK politicians to form the Mindfulness All-Party Parliamentary Group and conduct a policy inquiry throughout 2014, Jamie took over as Director in 2015 to launch the seminal Mindful Nation UK report. He has since grown the Mindfulness Initiative into an influential policy institute, authoring and producing a series of publications and working with decision-makers around the world to integrate inner capacities and contemplative practice into the public policy landscape. Jamie was formerly Business Development Director for Headspace and has a background in psychology, climate change campaign communications and advertising. A teacher of insight meditation, his mentors have included Rob Burbea, Stephen Batchelor and Christina Feldman.

Rosie Bell

Rosie Bell is a writer and communications advisor, and frequent collaborator with the Mindfulness Initiative. With an academic background in philosophy & literature and MA in International Public and Political Communication, her work is currently focused upon public narratives surrounding the climate movement, and the role of inner capacities in societal change. Alongside training as a mindfulness teacher, Rosie brings a background in performance to her decade of creative work with NGOs, social change initiatives and wellbeing innovators.

Professor Christine Wamsler

Christine Wamsler is Professor of Sustainability Science at LUCSUS and director of the Contemplative Sustainable Futures Program. She is an internationally-renowned expert in sustainable development and associated (material and cognitive) transformation processes with 25 years of experience, both in theory and practice. Her work has shaped international debates and increased knowledge on personal, collective, institutional and policy transformations in a context of climate change. She has written more than 200 papers, chapters and reports on these issues. Her publications are regularly cited and used for practice, theory and policy development, including by the Intergovernmental Panel on Climate Change (IPCC).

About The Mindfulness Initiative

The Mindfulness Initiative grew out of a programme of mindfulness teaching for politicians in the UK Parliament, and provides the secretariat to the Mindfulness All-Party Parliamentary Group. The Initiative works with legislators around the world who practice mindfulness and helps them to make trainable capacities of heart and mind serious considerations of public policy. It investigates the benefits, limitations, opportunities and challenges in accessing and implementing mindfulness and compassion training and educates leaders, service-commissioners and the general public based on these findings. Visit www.themindfulnessinitiative.org to find out more.

About Lund University Centre For Sustainability Studies (LUCSUS)

LUCSUS is a world-class centre for sustainability research, teaching and impact. A pioneer in transdisciplinary research and collaboration, it combines critical perspectives with solutions-based approaches to sustainability challenges such as climate change. The centre is home to three of the world's most influential researchers,[1] notably Professor Christine Wamsler, who is also the founder and director of the Contemplative Sustainable Futures Program. The Program's aim is to create space and opportunities for knowledge development, learning and networking on the role of human inner dimensions for sustainability. More generally, the mission is to relieve suffering, and support a more sustainable and just world through a scientific understanding of the mind for societal and planetary well-being. The Program supports ground-breaking research with real-world impact: new science on the role of the mind for social change and transformation. Visit www.lucsus.lu.se and www.contemplative-sustainable-futures.com to find out more.

Contents

Box references
Box 1: p11, Box2: p16, Box 3: p19, Box 4: p22, Box 5: p29, Box 6: p34, Box 7: p40, Box 8: p49, Box 9: p58, Box 10: p60

Executive Summary

Climate change is a physical reality, demanding urgent political and practical solutions. But its inner dimension, overlooked entirely by mainstream approaches, is a crisis of relationship. Currently the world is failing to implement solutions of the rate, scale and depth required to meaningfully address climate change within a closing window of opportunity for mitigation and adaptation. This grave shortcoming is rooted in the same pathology that drives the crisis: **lack of conscious connection with ourselves, with others and with the world we share.** While the consequences of our actions wreak havoc within an interconnected and increasingly fragile ecosystem, we continue to think and behave as if we are independent, and in competition with others to meet our needs. The same shared mindset of **separateness** that drives social alienation and exploitative human behaviours throughout society also inhibits sustainability responses at all levels. Meanwhile the mental health impacts of the climate crisis drive unsustainable behaviour and impede positive action, contributing to a **vicious cycle between mind and climate.**

In concert with a growing body of leading sustainability experts and with the Intergovernmental Panel on Climate Change (IPCC) reporting in 2021/22, this report calls urgently for policy attention to the neglected inner dimension of the climate crisis; in addressing both its **root causes** and **leverage points for change.** It examines the relevance of **mindfulness** and **compassion** practices in restoring the kinds of connection fundamental to individual and collective health at all times - and those of utmost importance in policy approaches to our current global sustainability crises.

Mindfulness - a mode of awareness with particular qualities, and compassion - an important psychological motivation system, are innate, trainable human capacities foundational to healthy connection with ourselves, with others and with nature. These relationships form the bedrock of our behaviour towards the world, and underpin our agency to effect meaningful change. Both mindfulness and compassion can be cultivated through **evidence-based practice**, and increased availability of training among decision-makers and wider populations is an enabling factor in more integrative and transformative sustainability responses. The insights and conclusions presented have clear implications for policy-making, and recommendations follow at the end of the document.

1: Fundamentals of connection

The interdependent faculties of **mind, body and heart** responsible for conscious connection are often disrupted and deprioritised. Cultivating these relational abilities is a fundamental necessity in overcoming the individual and collective fragmentation, alienation and insensitivity that drives the climate crisis. Mindfulness and compassion training can support numerous aspects of inner and outer reconnection.

1.1 Mind

The mind not only perceives but assembles the reality we see, hear and feel; shaped always by pre-existing tendencies that direct our foundational faculties of **attention** and **receptivity.** Distractions and biases continually disrupt our perceptual links to the world around us, and the digital economy amplifies these tendencies: at a time of existential crisis we are sorely disconnected from reality. Mindfulness training can empower us to bring open awareness to what is happening around us, and to shift **perspectives** to connect with a greater range of possible understanding.

1.2 Mind-body

At a societal scale, lack of connection with the **body** compounds our disregard for the natural world it belongs to. Depreciation of **body sensation** likewise limits the understanding available to us in addressing urgent challenges. Mindfulness practice can help us to reconnect with bodily intelligence.

Conversely, without awareness and self-regulation, perceived **threat** can trigger bodily responses that shut down our ability to connect with ourselves, others and the world - a pervasive driver of social fragmentation. Mindful self-connection helps us to understand and regulate these embodied tendencies, helping us to overcome social division and summon the collective effort to meet our shared challenges.

1.3 Mind-body-heart

The feelings that bond us with others and that which we love are commonly considered the territory of **heart**. Whereas these qualities are undervalued by a hyper-rational culture, our evolutionary inheritance of social connection and collaboration is equally central to humanity's flourishing, never more than in our current crisis. Indeed the cultural tendency to **devalue feeling** inhibits emotional connection with nature, and with the ecological consequences of exploitative behaviours. Mindfulness and compassion can both play a central role in re-activating heart connection.

2 Connection and the climate crisis

Chapter 2 explores particular ways in which a mindset of disconnection interacts with the climate crisis. Here mindful and compassionate reconnection is crucial to resilience and engagement amid inner and outer climate impacts - helping us address the conditions that have brought the crisis about, and overcome barriers to action.

2.1 Staying with the trouble

Climate change is a painful reality to connect with, and **avoidance** is a common coping strategy. Remaining engaged in order to respond calls on robust inner resources. Compassion practice can strengthen this resource, and help us regulate negative emotions that impede action. Mindfulness teaching likewise emphasises **turning towards and working through difficult feelings**. Mindful enquiry into distress at individual and collective levels can help us reshape the inner and outer conditions contributing to our predicament.

The mental health impacts of the climate crisis compound both unsustainable behaviour and inertia. Cultivating **psychological resilience** and **positive emotion** through mindfulness and compassion can help us turn a vicious circle of mind and climate into a regenerative spiral of individual and planetary wellbeing.

2.2 Joined-up world

The mass behaviours that drive the climate crisis are founded upon a **worldview** characterised by **separateness**. The same atomised view contributes to a dangerous illusion of powerlessness in the face of large-scale challenges. Shared worldviews govern mass behaviour and thus represent a deep leverage point for positive change. Practices like mindfulness and compassion can help us both to examine our own belief systems, and to nurture a worldview and mode of perception that treats the world and the people in it as profoundly connected. Accordingly, they can reciprocally enhance our sense of **nature connection**; a critical motivator of pro-environmental behaviour. And whereas **polarisation** allows vested interests to marginalise climate as a political issue, mindfulness and compassion practices can directly reduce the tendency to inhabit an 'us-and-them' worldview.

2.3 Intention and action

Widespread knowledge about the climate crisis has not translated into appropriate action at the level of leadership or sustainable behaviour on the part of mass society. Beneath this urgent problem lies a universal pattern of disconnection: there are important **gaps between what we know, what we want, and what we do**. First, at individual and societal levels, we often don't tend to **want** what we know to be good for us. Outdated adaptive drives (and the market forces that amplify them) have shaped an extractive

consumer culture, whose impacts are felt disproportionately by vulnerable regions and communities. By questioning internalised patterns governing consumption habits, and by cultivating qualities like appreciation and care, mindfulness and compassion practices can help reorient our 'wanting' toward sustainability at individual and societal levels.

Next, regardless of our best intentions, we may not always be in touch with our **values**. Cultural habits can make it particularly difficult for us to connect with ethical intentions. Mindfulness and compassion practices can help attune our **inner compass**; the innate, embodied discernment that supports ethical decision-making.

Finally, even when we know what we want, we aren't always in control of our actions, thanks to involuntary impulses, entrenched habits and a sophisticated 'autopilot'. The digital economy hacks and profits from these **reactive tendencies**, locking us into patterns of **automatic, unsustainable behaviour.** The distinction between reaction and considered **response** is a central pillar of mindfulness teaching. Practitioners learn to bring awareness to their impulses and habits, consciously reconnecting intention, action and consequence and thus helping to overcome the **values-action gap** that limits climate action at all scales.

Conclusion

Recent IPCC reports on climate change, mitigation and adaptation are unequivocal: time is running out for climate solutions of the scale and depth necessary to avoid catastrophe. Research confirms that a critical relational dimension is missing from mainstream sustainability approaches: if we go on treating climate change purely as an external, technical challenge, solutions will continue to elude us. This report however gives cause for hope, revealing **vast inner potential to activate outer change**. Its insights are relevant in addressing the root causes of climate change, mitigating its impacts, and overcoming cognitive and emotional barriers to action. Above all the report highlights an urgent need to integrate external approaches with inner work, and leaders who grasp and respond to this need will be those best equipped to implement genuine, transformative climate action now and in the future. Mindfulness and compassion are among the evidence-based, trainable inner capacities critical to this approach, and recommendations follow as to how decision-makers may begin integrating these into public policy for sustainability.

Introduction

Introduction

"Mindfulness and compassion are key to reconnecting with yourself and with others. In an age of divisive politics and constant distraction, they are a vital antidote to hate narratives and us-versus-them mindsets. They help us to stay connected with the wider whole and the longer term, and act as if these mattered."

– Heather Grabbe, Director of the Open Society European Policy Institute and Professor of Political Science

Most large-scale climate action to date has focused upon technical solutions to physical problems. Increasingly however, voices in the sustainability field warn that neglect of **human inner factors** driving the climate crisis leaves theories of change wanting; in part explaining the failure of current policies to deliver adequate response.[2] "Inner transition" towards sustainable behaviour is referenced explicitly by the latest reporting from the Intergovernmental Panel on Climate Change (IPCC), and a groundbreaking research review highlights the need to integrate external solutions with internal approaches.[3] In related work, influential scholars and practitioners have begun to identify a worldview of **disconnection** - a cultural narrative that treats individuals as separate from one another and from the natural world - as the common thread of our interrelated socio-ecological crises.[4]

Connection is inescapable. We embodied human beings are fundamentally embedded in a complex web of **interdependency**. We have always been totally dependent upon each other and our environment for survival - and now that we have become a global civilisation, our actions have global consequences. What we too often lack in terms of connection relates to its conscious or inner dimension - an understanding and a feeling of connection, and the beliefs, values and choices associated with them. Accordingly, alongside related factors such as fear, denial and disempowerment, the crises that we currently face are rooted in a failure to acknowledge the **wholeness** of our world and act as if we are part of it. Our every assault on our environment is founded upon a false idea of separation: from the assumption that we can harm 'the planet' without harming ourselves to the mistaken belief that it is possible to throw anything *away*. What we must understand together with the direst urgency is that there is no away; there is no truly separate other. We require widespread ways to reconnect with an experience of *here* and of *us*.

Environmental destruction is literally senseless: it reflects our collective failure to feel the harm we create. Implicated in this sensory failure is an internal rift. We are disconnected not only from our environment but also from ourselves. All too commonly we are unconscious of our emotions, our bodies, and our deeper sense of what is most important, with innumerable causes from denial and trauma to digital distractions and endemic busyness. Furthermore, **disconnection from self, from others and from nature** reinforce each other.[5] For instance, poor body awareness reduces our ability to understand and empathise with the emotions of others.[6]

This report explores the role of **mindfulness** and **compassion** in strengthening the cognitive and emotional foundations of **connection**. These **innate and trainable capacities** have potential to become powerful enablers of inner and outer reconnection, fostering greater resilience and engagement, and activating more decisive responses to our global sustainability crises.[7]

Key definitions: Mindfulness and Compassion

Mindfulness is a natural capacity that enables people to pay attention intentionally to present-moment experience, inside themselves and in their environment, with an attitude of openness, allowing, curiosity and care.

Compassion is an inner motivational system that combines the capacity to engage with and feel moved by suffering, with a will to help.[8] Like mindfulness, compassion can be cultivated through evidence-based practice.

We draw upon the emerging evidence base linking inner and outer transformation to sustainability, and broader academic literature on the pro-environmental and prosocial impact of mindfulness and compassion training, as well as the 10,000+ peer-reviewed articles that document the wider benefits of these interventions to individuals' health, functioning, and relationships.[9] In addition the report is based on 25 in-depth interviews that we conducted with national and transnational politicians and other policymakers, an online survey among leading experts working on inner aspects of the climate crisis and an extensive consultation process.[10] The result is a jumping-off point for a more informed and nuanced debate about how to better intervene on a long neglected front in the struggle towards sustainability.

Chapter One of this report concerns fundamental aspects of human connection, and the ways in which mindfulness and compassion always serve and enrich our conscious interface with reality and each other, even in the face of great disruption. **Chapter Two** explores the particular ways in which disconnection contributes to our most urgent global crisis. We discuss the many interactions between mindfulness, compassion, human connection and sustainability, and argue that by restoring conscious connection we increase not only personal resilience amid adversity, but also our chances of addressing the root causes of the crisis, and **mobilising change**.

Some clarifications

Advocacy of inner work in a social change context requires familiar caveats – particularly when the work in question is so gradual as cultivating mindfulness and compassion, and the context so urgent as climate change. When "the world is on fire", transformational approaches are hard to sell. But as we shall explore, they can help us to move more quickly and effectively in the longer term.

Importantly, we don't claim that current practical and policy approaches to climate change are wrong. The interventions outlined here are not offered as an alternative solution, but to activate more integrated approaches. Indeed, from policy negotiation and implementation to public debate and community resilience, we no longer have time to treat inner capacities as if they were not part of the real world. Research shows that approaches that link systems change with behavioural, cultural, and psychological considerations can lead to the most lasting impact.[11]

While we don't suggest that mindfulness and compassion are sufficient on their own to effect radical change, we argue that these innate human capacities are fundamental to conscious connection: at all times, and particularly in delivering more robust climate action. Not all interventions are equal however, and the outcomes we describe are usually associated with significant time investment in high quality, evidence-based training (see Box 4). For instance, mindfulness research demonstrates brain and behaviour changes from interventions of just a few minutes or hours,[12] but studies suggest that lasting impacts on pro-environmental behaviours take longer.[13]

Similarly, change at collective, organisational and systems levels requires more time and investment in research and policy. While thousands of trials demonstrate the effectiveness of mindfulness and compassion interventions in a clinical context, studies that examine direct causation of prosocial outcomes are at an early stage. For instance, while positive relationships between mindfulness and sustainable consumption can be demonstrated, it cannot yet be assumed that current forms of mindfulness training lead directly and causally to sustainable consumption behaviour. However, evidence suggests that mindfulness can create preconditions for such changes.[14]

Finally, to whom are these recommendations directed? The 'we' that appears throughout takes multiple, interlocking forms that a given reader may or may not own - we who are implicated in driving climate change; we who feel its impacts; we who are empowered in large ways and small to alter its course. We who hold power and we who hold power to account. Certainly, these practices may currently be inaccessible to many people - not least those most vulnerable to climate impacts - and 'we' aren't suggesting that 'you' meditate to feel better about the devastation that others have created. While it wouldn't make sense to exclude any person or group from a call to connection in a time of crisis, we hope that this report resonates particularly with decision-makers – as well as the practitioners and advocates taking inner capacity-building into the world of climate action.

"The IPCC conclusions haven't changed in 15 years. 'There is climate change. Humans are causing it. It has great impacts. We have policy instruments to solve it at a reasonable cost.' Why is it not happening? Why is making changes so difficult? The IPCC and European Commision are now trying more to understand that... how can these elements of inner qualities and capacities be included?"

– **Bas Eickhout**, Member of the European Parliament and deputy chairman of the Greens–European Free Alliance, co-author of the 2007 IPCC report

Building on previous work: lessons from COP and research

This report and related research builds on a programme of work conducted over several years, demonstrating that both scholars and policymakers increasingly see human inner qualities and capacities as vital in supporting sustainability and addressing climate change.[15] The urgent need to consider the inner dimension of sustainability is likewise reflected in the 2022 IPCC report.[16]

At the most recent UNFCCC Conferences of the Parties (COP25 & 26), researchers investigated decision-makers' views about the inner qualities and mindsets that can support negotiating and activating climate action. A related study included large-scale surveys and semi-structured interviews with COP attendees; both negotiators and observers.[17] Participants demonstrated compelling agreement regarding the need to address mindsets to support new ways of communicating and collaborating. The results show furthermore that such change requires improved relational qualities and modes of knowing, being and acting.

These outcomes were confirmed in 2020-21 by the first systematic review of academic literature that analysed how the links between inner and outer transformation to support climate action are portrayed and understood in current research.[18] Based on these findings, the review proposes an integrated model of inner-outer transformation that shows how clusters of transformative inner qualities and capacities are related to worldviews, beliefs and values that delineate our relationships with ourselves, others, and the world.[19] These in turn influence our agency to support change at individual, collective and systems levels.

The review also highlights a potential role for mindfulness and compassion in this context - so long as they are not applied in an instrumentalised way, stripped of ecological and social awareness. Evidence shows that mindfulness and compassion are linked to all clusters of transformative qualities identified in the model of inner-outer transformation. The authors recommend that it is now crucial to explore if, and how, related approaches can best be oriented toward sustainability and mainstreamed into current institutional and policy structures. This report is an important first step in this direction.

1

Fundamentals of Connection

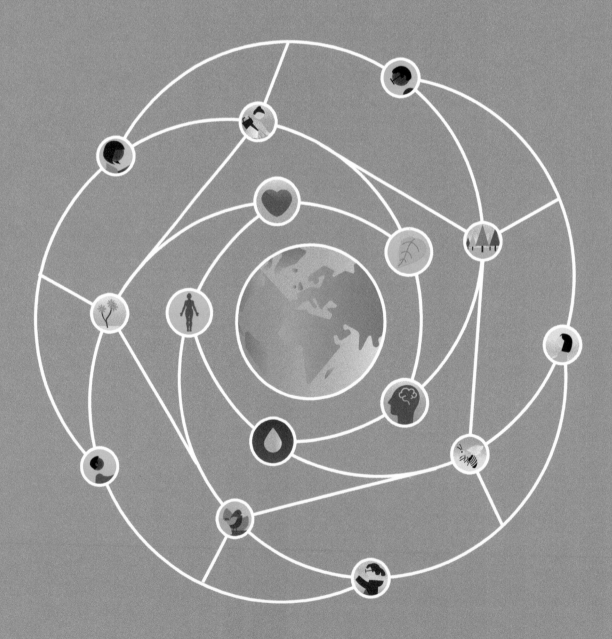

Fundamentals of Connection

"We need to approach the climate crisis from a position of consciousness, and of conscience, as well as science. I think that's where mindfulness and compassion can be absolutely key. They can make that connection between the mind, body and heart - in an evidence-based way."

– Chris Ruane, Member of the British Parliament for 20 years and founder of the UK All-Party Parliamentary Group on Mindfulness

Humans possess the capacity for deep conscious connection with ourselves, with others and with nature. But the qualities that serve these relationships are often de-prioritised, underdeveloped and neglected. This chapter establishes the role of mindfulness and compassion in mediating fundamental aspects of connection, and how these faculties can be trained in the service of better relationship. In doing so it addresses separately what is inseparable. Whereas we distinguish for the purpose of discussion domains of **mind, body and heart,** ongoing developments in social cognitive neuroscience support understanding of conscious beings as *intra*connected[20] - a perspective central to many wisdom traditions.[21] We discuss the ways in which cultivation of mindfulness and compassion can support these spheres of connection - healing the relationship between estranged inner capacities and allowing them to function and flourish together.

We turn first to **mind**, the principal medium of conscious interface with the world. Fed by outer stimuli, the mind not only perceives but assembles the world we see, hear and feel; shaped by pre-existing tendencies that direct our faculties of **attention** and **receptivity**. We discuss the distractions and biases that disrupt perceptual links to reality, together with opportunities for training the mind to reinforce connection. In a world designed for attentional hijack, mindfulness practice can restore us to some power over the content of our minds. It helps us to relate to experience just as it is - remaining connected to unfamiliar or challenging information and shifting **perspective** to connect with a greater range of possible understanding.

A culture of disembodiment underpins our exploitation of the world we are part of. Next therefore, we explore the importance of mindfulness to **body** connection; cultivating respect for bodily sensation as an arena of knowledge and broadening the scope of understanding available to us in relating to and addressing our collective challenges. We acknowledge the ways in which **neurophysiological** systems can both support and interfere with connection to others and the world, and outline the role of mindful self-connection in re-establishing agency in these conditions.

Finally, we address the domain of connection popularly associated with the **heart** - that of relational bonds and empathic feelings. Endemic disconnection and lack of care for others and the environment belies the highly evolved human capacities for care and collaboration that are critical in collective response to the climate crisis. We discuss the central role of mindfulness and compassion practices in strengthening such fundamental aspects of **social connection**.

While links to the current crisis appear where appropriate throughout Chapter 1, we also intend these three dimensions of conscious connection to be understood as foundational to what follows. While mind-body-heart risks sounding like a trite slogan, these are deeply serious considerations. Encompassed within these domains are all the faculties we have available to **understand ourselves, relate to others, connect with nature and act effectively.**

1.1
Fundamentals of Connection: Mind

"There are many changes to make over the next 10 years, and each of us will take different steps along the way, but all of us start the transformation in one place: our mindset."

– Christiana Figueres, Former Executive Secretary of the United Nations Framework Convention on Climate Change (UNFCCC) 2010-2016.

1.1.1 Reclaiming Attention

"We're swamped with so much information, so cultivating attention is key - the ability to focus on and retain information so as to really discern what is important."

– Anne Louise Friedrichsen, Wellbeing Advisor at the Directorate-General for Human Resources and Security, European Commission

Attention is the foundation of our perceptual connection with the world. If we want to know what's happening - let alone actively solve a problem - a basic condition is that we pay attention.[22] However, our attentional hierarchy is ill-adapted to our modern world, and even worse to addressing a long-term, slow-moving and uncertain threat such as the climate crisis.[23] Evolution has tuned our drives to prioritise information relevant to immediate survival objectives in a prehistoric landscape: grabbing what tastes good, evading threat, finding a mate. The distracting power of these basic drives has troubled us since the dawn of civilisation, with much social philosophy devoted to liberating attention in the service of 'higher' thought and feeling.[24]

In the current internet era, connecting with what matters involves not only mastering these primal adaptive drives, but also resisting the global political and economic powers that 'hack' and amplify them for their own purposes.[25] At the moment of our greatest peril, we have never been more distracted from what is happening around us. Media subvert our relationship with the world by optimising news to capture attention, ratcheting up anxiety and threat perception.[26] At our first sign of boredom or discomfort, we are conditioned to reach for a device that blots it all out with apps designed to turn attention into profit. Smartphone use corrodes interpersonal connection[27] - researchers describe as 'absent-presence' the phenomenon of people sharing space while ignoring each other.[28] It also radically disrupts our capacity for uninterrupted presence in nature.[29] Digital technology use is negatively correlated with nature connectedness: a cornerstone of sustainable behaviours.[30] This escalating social and environmental alienation is implicated in the climate crisis, not least because strong relationships are critical in shifting attitudes and behaviour, and fomenting collective action.[31]

Curbing the excesses of the attention economy requires structural change - but at the same time we may also empower ourselves to remain present with the world. Indeed this kind of self-emancipation may be a prerequisite of systemic change in the current era; restoring the awareness of circumstances that underpins individual and collective agency. Mindfulness practice can facilitate such empowerment, because it includes a particular kind of attention training. Through repeated exercises, including formal meditation and behavioural practises, we can train the 'muscle' of the mind to notice when it has strayed from its chosen object and to return there. Practitioners learn to attend to attention itself, getting to know its habitual patterns and how they may serve or undermine intentions.[32] Mindfulness training has been shown to protect against proactively distracting stimuli[33] and to enhance self-control.[34] In other words, practitioners of mindfulness are learning to reclaim their attention for their own purposes. From this foundation it becomes possible to redistribute awareness in ways that better meet our needs as individuals, as groups and as a global living system.

The Evidence for Mindfulness Training

The number of academic studies examining the effect of mindfulness on sustainability has increased dramatically over the last 5-10 years and these build upon an already extensive evidence base. A 2021 review identified nearly 17,000 academic publications (approximately 15,000 articles and 2,000 reviews) referring to mindfulness in the title, abstract, or keywords.

Mindfulness has been found to positively affect a wide range of outcomes across health, wellbeing, performance and relationships. The highest quality of evidence comes so far from clinical studies addressing common mental health concerns such as depression, anxiety, stress, over-eating and addiction along with managing long-term physical conditions such as chronic pain and cancer.[35] Outcomes for Mindfulness-Based Interventions tend to be comparable to other evidence-based treatment, with evidence of superiority for tackling depression and smoking.[36] Recent meta-analyses also found positive effects on:

- Wellbeing and non-clinical mental health,[37] including via digital apps and websites.[38]

- Workplace well-being, compassion, and job satisfaction, reduction in occupational stress, burnout, mental distress, and somatic complaints.[39]

- Cognitive performance, such as attention, memory and self-control.[40]

- Prosocial behaviour,[41] compassionate helping and reduced prejudice and retaliation.[42]

- Physiological indices of stress including immune system response,[43] and blood pressure.[44]

- Length of telomeres[45] (structures found at the ends of our chromosomes, erosion of which is associated with ageing).

Evidence in non-clinical areas is currently less robust and positive effects may be over-reported, with most research at an early stage or limited by methodological weakness such as small sample sizes or lack of active controls.[46]

What neuroscience tells us

The neuroscience of mindfulness training has attracted popular attention since 2005, when Harvard researcher Sarah Lazar first published findings that meditation can change the structure of the brain, thickening areas of the cortex that help control attention and emotions. While research is still nascent and caution is required, this early message that "mindfulness can literally change your brain"[47] is a helpful counterpoint to a popular assumption that as adults we are 'stuck' with the mind as it is. Studies show that practice impacts the neural correlates of capacities important to adult development.

Research suggests that mindfulness-based interventions may increase activity and efficiency in brain areas and networks underlying attention and body awareness. Studies show reduced activity and volume in brain areas involved in stress and anxiety experiences, particularly the amygdala.

The majority of scientific evidence for mindfulness relates to eight-week courses. However, research has also investigated the effects of shorter mindfulness training and one-off sessions. One study examined reductions in pain and associated brain changes after only four 20-minute sessions of mindfulness delivered over four days.[48] The findings showed significant decreases in pain intensity and unpleasantness. These decreases were observed during mindfulness practice and were associated with increased activation in attention regulation areas as well as reduced activity in areas linked to pain perception.

Other studies used brief mindfulness practices over a longer period (for example, at least ten minutes per day on at least five days per week for 16 weeks) and found improvements in brain functioning associated with attention processing.[49] Another linked increases in brain activity with improved attention processing after only three hours of mindfulness training over five days.

"We are so focussed on digital stimuli that as a counterforce we have a growing need to look inside, and also to look to real and physical things such as nature. There is this growing fear that we are being alienated from our physical reality."

– Yoko Alender, Member of the Estonian Parliament and chair of its Environment Committee.

1.1.2 **Increasing Receptivity**

"The land is the real teacher. All we need as students is mindfulness. Paying attention is a form of reciprocity with the living world, receiving the gifts with open eyes and open heart."

– Robin Wall Kimmerer, Professor of Environmental and Forest Biology, Director of the Centre for Native Peoples and the Environment at the State University of New York

Commonly we assume that perceptual connection with the world is straightforward and rational: that we collect information and then base our beliefs on the evidence of our senses. We think that we perceive the world 'as it is'. But in fact we more often see it as we think it is (See Fig 1.). The mind imposes prior knowledge automatically: classifying not only objects but also complex experiences within existing models of the world.[50] These frameworks of ideas are not an error to be corrected - they are essential for navigating life in an environment that contains far too much information to process directly.[51] However, such cognitive shortcuts also entail some level of disconnect between perception and reality.

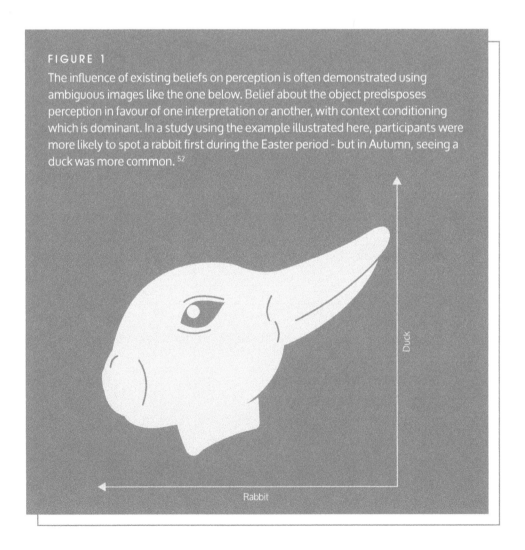

FIGURE 1

The influence of existing beliefs on perception is often demonstrated using ambiguous images like the one below. Belief about the object predisposes perception in favour of one interpretation or another, with context conditioning which is dominant. In a study using the example illustrated here, participants were more likely to spot a rabbit first during the Easter period - but in Autumn, seeing a duck was more common. [52]

Duck

Rabbit

Over time our internal models become less accurate and useful if they are not updated with new information. However, a common aspect of cognition leads us to reject information that contradicts them.[53] This bias towards existing beliefs and judgements can seriously limit our ability to notice new threats and possibilities, reducing our capacity to respond skilfully to a changing world. At a global scale, it has contributed to a 50-year delay in meaningful action on the science of climate change. Stuck in old mindsets, we remain disconnected from the urgent realities of a changing planet.

The capacity for mindfulness can counteract this change-blindness - in fact, one school of thought even defines mindfulness as consciously looking for what is new and different, and questioning preconceived ideas.[54] The search for new information in an object or situation is an act of continual reconnection; a conscious step beyond assumptions in an effort to perceive reality as it arises.

The attitudes of mind that characterise mindful awareness include **openness, allowing, curiosity** and **kindness**. Here, to be 'open' is to put aside preconceptions as far as possible, the better to receive experience as it arises rather than imposing knowledge upon it. 'Allowing' refers to non-resistance to current experience, whatever its content. To be 'curious' is to develop an appetite for finding out through inquiry. Finally, 'kind' awareness welcomes its object with an attitude of care. Practising each of these interrelated qualities amplifies the others, holding wide the 'bandwidth' of perception and enhancing our receptivity to whatever is arising.

This practised receptivity and challenging of existing mindsets is foundational in questioning current, unsustainable habits and inviting curiosity into different possible ways of life.[55] The principle of 'allowing' is sometimes misconstrued as antithetical to seeking change - however, denial of current reality is a poor foundation for a constructive response. Comprehending things as they are is a crucial first step in responding appropriately to our circumstances.

BOX 3: EXPLORE FURTHER
Mindfulness courses and types of practice

Although many 'self-help' books and apps are now available, some with an emerging evidence base of their own, most research into mindfulness has tested in-person teaching. A typical mindfulness course includes weekly sessions over 6-12 weeks and increasingly involves aspects of compassion training. Mindfulness courses include formal and informal practice instruction, education content and teacher-led 'inquiry' into participant experiences to facilitate embodied learning. Informal practice is the cultivation of moment-to-moment mindfulness in daily activities.

The components of mindfulness courses vary depending on their context and desired outcomes, but those that adhere closely to academic evidence usually share core elements.[56] Most peer-reviewed research papers on mindfulness concern the eight-week Mindfulness-Based Stress Reduction (MBSR) course developed in the late 1970s by Jon Kabat-Zinn, and its many adaptations like Mindfulness-Based Cognitive Therapy (MBCT), Mindfulness-Based Pain Management (MBPM) or Mindfulness-Based Relapse Prevention (MBRP).

Some leading pioneers in the field have developed a framework for defining Mindfulness-Based Interventions (MBIs) wherein fixed characteristics (the warp) can be interwoven with novel elements depending on its application (the weft).[57] Others eschew this approach and have established new curricula from first principles, although few of these courses are as yet supported by empirical research. Since 2017, mindfulness approaches have increasingly been integrated in education for sustainability, showing positive initial results.[58]

1.1.3 Perspective-Taking and Cognitive Flexibility

"Mindfulness can help improve mutual understanding by creating space for considering any serious, intractable or complex situation, both logically and emotionally."

– Scott Brison, former Member of the Canadian Parliament and President of the Canadian Treasury Board

Connecting with a multifaceted and changing world and meeting its challenges in their ambiguity and complexity requires us to step repeatedly beyond a fixed point of view: to grasp reality from different perspectives. Inability to shift perspective leaves us disconnected from countless possible ways of understanding and contributes among other things to climate change denial, rigidity in negotiation, and inadequate problem-solving.[59] Along with the personality trait of openness, perspective-taking is associated with sustainable attitudes.[60]

Mindfulness practice has been shown to develop cognitive flexibility: the mental ability to switch between concepts, and to comprehend multiple concepts simultaneously which is necessary to integrate and to move between different perspectives.[61] Studies indicate that the practice is specifically helpful in developing greater flexibility in perspective-taking.[62] Participant feedback from mindfulness interventions often references an increased ability to gain perspective, and numerous studies on mindful leadership suggest that mindfulness helps leaders develop alertness to multiple perspectives.[63] Certain studies define mindfulness in terms of the ability to view objects and situations from multiple points of view, and to shift perspectives depending on context.[64] By contrast, they define 'mindlessness' as a state in which the individual adheres to a single perspective and acts automatically.

The effectiveness of mindfulness in many of its health applications hangs upon the improved capacity to gain perspective on mental processes.[65] For example, in treating difficult experiences as objects of awareness and curiosity, practitioners avoid becoming absorbed or over-identified with their content: the origin of the well-known expression "I am not my thoughts". This is the development of 'meta-cognitive awareness', also known as de-centering. Reducing identification with thoughts and interrupting the related tendency to believe them as the truth ("thoughts are not facts") allows us in turn to take our own perspectives on the world less personally, and admit challenges to our point of view with less friction. Thus mindfulness can facilitate interpersonal connection and cooperation in spaces where differing views have led previously to impasse - indeed, politicians have stated that mindfulness training helps them to "disagree better".[66] Better perspective-taking, cognitive flexibility and active de-centring have clear implications for the high-stakes negotiation and complex collective decision-making necessitated by global climate governance.

"Mindfulness is not something you do in half an hour a week and then forget about. It's something that you are constantly practising. It changes your outlook on things... It helps you to be calm, to think in the moment, to consider the challenges that you face from different angles."

- Tim Loughton MP, Member of the British Parliament and Co-Chair of the All-Party Parliamentary Group on Mindfulness

The importance of 'social mindfulness'

The term 'mindfulness' is now used to describe all kinds of practices, many of which would more accurately be described as simple attention training or relaxation exercises. Short or shallow interventions may have many important short-term, individual benefits, but are unlikely to deliver the prosocial and sustainability benefits we describe in this document.

It is likely, however, that high-quality training programmes that cultivate mindfulness over longer periods are a strong net-positive for society. For example, a recent meta-analysis has found that trials of mindfulness training show improvements in pro-sociality, even where course material contains no explicit pro-social components.[67] This effect is likely due in part to the pedagogy and teacher-training of quality mindfulness-based programmes, which are explicitly geared towards building an ethical context for learning. This ethical component tends to be transmitted implicitly however - partly to avoid interventions being seen as ideological.[68]

We cannot assume just because mindfulness training seems to be socially and ecologically beneficial on balance, that this is true for all people or in all circumstances. Furthermore, existing benefits should not prevent the possibility that training design could evolve to become more reliably transformative.

A recent study found that a brief 'mindfulness induction' led those with an existing interconnected worldview to act more prosocially in an experimental task, but the induction influenced those with an individualistic worldview to respond less prosocially.[69] Crucially, the trial also found that when participants were **primed** towards an individualistic self-view this led to less prosocial responses, while the priming of an interconnected self-view led to more prosociality.[70] Although the outcomes of these very short inductions are not comparable with full mindfulness courses and on-going regular practice, they do highlight the importance of how course content is **framed**. Do participants aim simply to regulate stress, attention or sleep, or do they intend to become a better friend, collaborator, leader or contributor to their community?

There is some evidence that the intention behind meditation practice develops naturally over time: from self-regulation, to self-exploration to self-liberation or 'compassionate service'.[71] However, scope undoubtedly exists for a more explicitly prosocial approach to introductory mindfulness training, which could expand its focus beyond individual wellbeing to wider societal and planetary wellbeing.

Mainstream mindfulness courses have tended to emphasise the individual - partly because research outcomes are easier to capture at an individual level, and partly because public policy organisations and research funders are largely structured with a focus on individual suffering. Courses include a combination of mindfulness practices, didactic education and teacher-led group inquiry, supporting participants to 'turn towards' distress with curiosity, and develop insight into its sources, mechanisms and relief. This same process of mindful inquiry can also be applied through a cultural and collective lens, supporting participants to develop a more complex and systemic understanding of how and why distress and human flourishing arise - and of their own role in this process. Indeed, early pioneers of secular-scientific mindfulness training intended this more systemic orientation, however over time research has focused the field toward individual outcomes.[72]

This renewed consideration of social context and broadening the aims of practice has been described as 'social mindfulness' - and the innovations that target sustainable attitudes and behaviours could further be termed 'ecological mindfulness'. Currently these are the strands of innovation most promising in terms of the benefits outlined in this report - see for example Box 10. As we shall discuss in Section 1.3.2, these formats may necessitate practices that explicitly cultivate prosocial affect - like care and compassion. The emerging field of social mindfulness furthermore understands practises as contingent upon existing societal structures. Teachers increasingly recognise that content and delivery must be grounded in cultural context in order to be appropriate to diverse groups.

1.2
Fundamentals of Connection: Mind-Body

"The borders to awareness are emotional and embodied, and at this point in time we urgently need practices that cultivate the ability to be deeply aware."

– Liam Kavanagh, author, cognitive scientist and co-founder of Life Itself Labs

1.2.1 Embodiment

Conscious connection is not solely the territory of the mind as commonly conceived. Indeed humanity's problem of disconnection stems in part from a conceptual separation of mind and body in the history of Western thought. Although many ancient wisdom traditions have long situated consciousness in both the mind and the body, body sensation is an arena of perception often devalued within contemporary thinking-dominated culture. Habitually we treat our bodies as "vehicles that carry our heads from meeting to meeting".[73] However, this rich source of information is more than just a side-show. Body sensation is an essential component of cognition - and thus our cultural disembodiment has profoundly negative implications for our relationship with the world. Endemic disconnection from our bodies has likewise limited our awareness of ourselves as embedded creatures that exist interdependently with our environment,[74] ultimately leading to exploitative and extractive attitudes and behaviour (see also Section 2.2). This schism even creeps into sustainability narratives; exemplified by the notion of saving 'the planet', as if this was something separate from ourselves.[75] Resulting approaches to problem-solving can risk prioritising abstract concepts over tangible realities.

At the cutting edge of neuro- and cognitive sciences, our historical mind-body dualism is undergoing a correction. Increasingly it is shown that thoughts and feelings arise dependent on the interaction between brain, body, and our physical and social environments.[76] Reasearch has found that body awareness is important for self-regulation, wellbeing, emotional intelligence and decision-making, and studies suggest that it is a precondition for social perspective-taking and empathy.[77] Importantly, neuroscience has found that we refer to our own felt experience to understand the experiences of others.[78] For example, when we listen to a friend describe a distressing event, we are also monitoring signals from our own body that help us to understand the emotions at play and discern an appropriate response.

Awareness of the body is an explicit foundation of mindfulness in all of its applications. Conversely mindfulness meditation can help us to observe and gain insight into the complex interactions between different bodily senses and mental experiences, leading to a more integrated sense of embodiment.[79] Contemporary evidence-based mindfulness training programmes like Mindfulness-Based Stress Reduction (MBSR) and Mindfulness-Based Cognitive Therapy (MBCT) emphasise the importance of developing intimacy with a felt sense of the body and, along with attention regulation, this forms a core learning objective.[80] Accordingly, mindfulness is associated with greater self-reported body awareness,[81] and research shows that the brain regions related to body awareness show greater activation and may increase in volume following training.[82] As well as foundational breathing practices, exercises like the 'body scan' and 'mindful movement' like gentle yoga and walking can help participants to tune in to important patterns of feeling, often neglected or repressed for a lifetime. As such they support not only self-knowledge and self-regulation, but also the discernment that we need to navigate throughout life - never more than in the current crisis. The embodied cognition mindfulness practice supports is foundational to an engaged understanding of ecological destruction - and appropriate response.

"Suppress what is difficult and stress is still happening in the body, physiologically. It's still affecting people, impacting wellbeing and decision-making, they're just not aware of it. Practising mindfulness can help us notice and interpret the subtle signals. To see more clearly what is actually going on, and face the reality of the situation with all the accompanying emotions."

– Nadine Andrews, Climate Psychology Alliance member and Principal Social Researcher for the Scottish Government

1.2.2 Managing Threat Response

The neurophysiological (brain-body) system is always operating in one of several modes, which dictate conditions in the mind and body in preparation for different types of interaction. As such they powerfully affect the social connections that underpin cooperation on shared challenges such as climate change - and understanding how to manage them can help unlock negotiation and collaboration in this urgent context. For example, in the so-called **'approach state'**, we 'rest and digest' or move towards pleasant stimuli such as food or friends. Described by scientists as the 'social engagement system', this mode is foundational to connection with others.[83] It is likewise important for approaching inner experience with openness and curiosity, and for nature connectedness. It requires a sense of trust and safety to come online. By contrast, the states that evolved to trigger reaction to threatening situations are known as the **'fight-flight' and 'freeze-faint' modes**.[84] Both were key to survival in prehistoric times, but are ill-adapted to many perceived threat situations in modern life: mechanisms that once assisted us in escaping predators can now be triggered by an email from the boss. Fight-flight mode elevates stress hormones, heart rate, breathing rate and sweating[85] and is associated with disordered thinking and perceptual narrowing.[86]

Neurophysiological states exert a powerful influence upon our **relationships** because we respond reflexively to cues in the words, voices and body language of others. Our nervous systems interact, threat breeding threat and safety breeding safety. This subtle feedback loop comprises a kind of 'social field' or atmosphere.[87] It might be imagined by comparing the idea of entering a room filled with friends to one full of strangers. How differently is the body held; the voice projected? Reaction to perceived threat limits our ability to empathise, connect with others and develop generative relationships, and engages a range of defence mechanisms like denial, distortion and disengagement.[88] Over time, fight-flight and freeze-faint modes leave us more prone to extremist views and othering dynamics,[89] fragmenting social and political groups (Section 2.2.3) and shrinking the space for collective action on shared problems - above all, climate change.

A significant branch of mindfulness training specifically addresses maladaptive threat responses and a robust body of evidence demonstrates its effectiveness.[90] Mindfulness can help us to notice when threat response is activated and engage in behaviours and exercises that foster the approach state. Whereas fight-flight mode conditions certain thinking patterns, breathing rates and body postures, the interaction also works in the opposite direction - for example, deliberate slow and deep breathing reduces activation.[91] The qualities of mindful attention introduced in Section 1.1.2 - openness, allowing, curiosity and care - are also inherent elements of the approach state and contribute to its activation. Developing these qualities means more than just acquiring tools to manage a triggered threat response: it reduces the likelihood of being triggered in the first place. Accordingly, neuroscientists have found that the brain region most implicated in fight-flight mode, reduces both in size and activity following mindfulness training.[92]

Real systemic conditions contribute to threat perception throughout society, and we do not suggest that individuals are responsible for absorbing the effects of toxic culture - or that they should practice to ignore threats to safety and wellbeing. However, the ability to shift these systemic conditions itself depends upon our inner capacities. The self-connection and self-regulation that help us to manage threat response also underpin the wider connection that we need to collaborate and co-create change.

"We risk a 'breakdown loop', where the state of the world creates negative states of mind leading to antisocial citizenship behaviours, which worsen the state of the world or prevent us from acting to improve it...we need to reverse that cycle and create a 'breakthrough loop.'"

– Alex Evans, author, founder of A Larger Us, former Campaign Director at Avaaz.

1.2.3 **Addressing Trauma**

"When I was 15, there was a shooting in my school. I was nearly killed, and my friend was killed. I was very traumatised, of course. I had a lot of anger. But it was the reason I got into politics.... I used mindfulness, meditation and connection to nature to heal my trauma. I had to go into deep layers of my life to survive it and engage with the world again."

– Alviina Alametsä, Member of the European Parliament serving on the Committee on Foreign Affairs

Activating threat response mode may be unavoidable, or even beneficial, during highly stressful or genuinely dangerous events. When a stressful experience falls within an individual's range of ability to process and integrate it - like perhaps, going into hospital for a planned operation - the body regulates itself afterwards, returning to a sense of safety and security. However, if an experience is "too much, too soon or too fast" relative to an individual's psycho-social resources - for example, a serious accident, disaster or assault - the mind becomes overwhelmed, does not integrate the experience, and therefore does not send signals of safety that would return the nervous system to its baseline state.[93] Instead the mind-body system becomes stuck at some level of continual threat perception, leading to a dysregulated nervous system and a dominant fight-flight or freeze-faint mode that is easily triggered. Dysregulation can exhibit as excessive busyness and exertion, or sometimes a dissociative, depressed shutdown.[94]

Depending on severity and compounding factors, the impact of dysregulation falls on a continuum between chronic or traumatic stress and complex Post Traumatic Stress Disorder (PTSD). Whether diagnosed as chronic stress or trauma, experts consider typical defence mechanisms to include psychological fragmentation, and disassociation or 'splitting', which manifests as a numbing or compartmentalisation of the psycho-social world.[95] Our coping mechanism disconnects us from parts of our own inner lives, from other people and the world around us. As we have discussed, this fragmentation is both a driver of unsustainable behaviour and a barrier to the kind of social solidarity and collective understanding needed to act meaningfully on climate change.

In recent years there has been a movement to recognise the 'trauma of everyday life', acknowledging the significant psychological injuries from family or school life that most people carry throughout adulthood.[96] However individual experience can not fully account for the nervous system dysregulation that we commonly carry. Research suggests that individuals and communities also carry *collective* trauma that is passed on behaviourally, such as 'intergenerational' trauma resulting from historic conflict, displacement, poverty, racism and oppression, interrelated with patterns of domestic abuse and violence.[97] To this we may add 'eco-trauma' - the dysregulation resulting from the continual threat of ecological and societal collapse.[98] Emerging research extends the definition of trauma to include this kind of chronic, collective Threat exposure.[99] Beyond individual health, this psychological burden has severe implications for social connection and our response to collective challenges, making us more likely to antagonise and to retreat from one another.[100]

Current therapeutic approaches to trauma focus upon rebuilding an individual's sense of connection and personal agency, as well as working consciously with the body to 'reset' the nervous system's normal cycles.[101] Mindfulness and compassion support all of these mechanisms.[102] Self-compassion practice can also help people recover from trauma and reduce PTSD symptoms, in part by addressing associated self-judgement and shame.[103] Furthermore, studies suggest that both mindfulness and self-compassion practices aid 'post-traumatic growth', through which people become more capable and resilient after experiencing great adversity.[104] Accordingly, in recent years, mindfulness-informed interventions such as Dialectical Behaviour Therapy (DBT) have been deployed to tackle PTSD.[105] Recognising the prevalence of nervous system dysregulation in the general population there has been a movement to make all mindfulness training more 'trauma-informed', adapting standard teaching protocols to identify everyday trauma and handle it more safely.[106]

BOX 5: KEY ISSUE

Is mindfulness practice for everyone?

Mindfulness is best understood as a natural human capacity, and many people are helped by cultivating it in a multitude of ways. However, it would be misleading to claim therefore that mindfulness *training programmes* are a panacea. Every person faces a unique set of circumstances and challenges and accordingly research has shown from the outset that the effectiveness of mindfulness practice differs with the individual. While many people will find a training programme helpful, others will not.

Occasionally, participants report unusual or unexpected experiences. For instance, reconnecting consciously with the body may bring encounters with feelings or memories that have been suppressed in the past as part of a coping mechanism.[107] This could prompt a variety of reactions, from curiosity at one end of the scale, to concern or distress at the other. A legacy of trauma in the nervous system may necessitate great care in tuning into sensation. This is one reason why self-compassion, or compassion for the body itself, can also be a crucial skill that facilitates reconnection.[108]

Further research is needed to better understand the origins and frequency of difficult experiences arising in mindfulness practice and how best to respond to them. This might ask, for example, under what circumstances it is appropriate to continue with mindfulness meditation, to change the type of practice, or to pause or stop altogether. Teachers should be alert to these experiences, and quality teacher-training organisations have established protocols for how best to manage them.

No psychological intervention is without risk. As with exercise and pharmaceuticals, those working in the field of mindfulness must develop an understanding of how to deploy practices skilfully so as to reduce the chance of harm. Clinical interventions working with severe symptoms and other vulnerabilities have found that adverse experiences occur in 0-10% of participants, and are no more common in interventions than control groups.[109] However many studies have not monitored harm in any way and, when they do, its relationship to mindfulness practices is not always clear. Appropriately then, this has become a major theme in the on-going work and research of leading mindfulness training organisations in recent years.[110]

1.3
Fundamentals of Connection: Mind-Body-Heart

"Love is the opening for regeneration. If we want to heal global warming, let's go to where love resides already: the human heart."

– Paul Hawken, author of *Drawdown: The Most Comprehensive Plan Ever Proposed to Reverse Global Warming* and *Regeneration: Ending the Climate Crisis in One Generation*

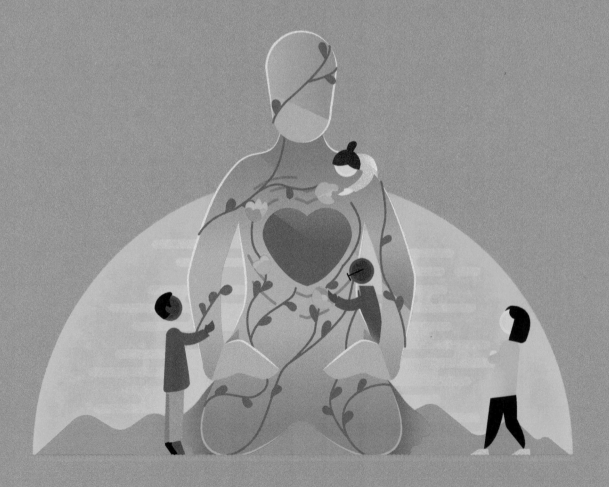

1.3.1 Emotional Intelligence

"The biggest deficit that we have in our society and in the world right now is an empathy deficit."

– Former US President Barack Obama

The Western Enlightenment thinking that separates mind from body, and thinking from feeling, tends to place less value on human social and emotional capacities than upon reasoning abilities such as IQ. This imbalance reflects in part a tendency to imagine humanity's success as a species in terms of competition; overlooking our equally potent ability to connect and collaborate (see also Section 2.2.1).[111] A pseudo-Darwinian narrative of 'survival of the fittest' informed a culture of aggressive individualism throughout the 20th Century, shaping not only exploitative attitudes to other species, but a competitive, fragmented social model.[112] However, a re-balancing of this story is underway. Scientists now understand human evolutionary success to be founded also upon shared meaning-making and cultural transmission, and the trend across time to extend the care and pro-sociality initially evolved for our closest kin to those ever more distant from us.[113] These relational abilities have made us the most collaborative species on the planet. Through cultural evolution, increasingly complex ideas have enabled us to connect in ever greater numbers and increasing specialisation - what sociobiologists call "ultrasociality".[114]

Enabling these collaborative tendencies is a highly developed composite faculty often described as Emotional Intelligence (EI or EQ). EQ includes empathy - the capacity to pick up on and share the feelings of another - but it is more broadly defined as the ability to perceive, process and manage one's own emotions and those of others.[115] As such it encompasses a range of social and relational skills such as perspective-taking and understanding others' motives.[116] EQ underpins self-awareness, self-control and productive relationships.[117] It is also associated with a broad range of skills like decision-making, academic achievement and job performance.[118] Without EQ we are cut off from the emotional signals within and around us. The cultural tendency to deprioritise EQ likewise depresses emotional connection with nature, and with the ecological consequences of exploitative behaviours.

A culture preoccupied with rationality and IQ is reflected in an education system that leaves our capacity for connection with self, others and nature sorely underdeveloped.[119] EQ can however be cultivated and learned throughout life, and Social and Emotional Learning (SEL) programmes are now commonplace in schools. Approaches to foster EQ generally include mindfulness components, and mindfulness training itself has been found to boost many aspects of emotional intelligence, including emotional clarity, emotion regulation, and empathy in both adults and children.[120] Mindfulness also facilitates better listening, communication and conflict resolution.[121] Accordingly, qualitative feedback from participants in mindfulness-based programmes points to positive effects upon interpersonal relationships.[122]

"Logic and reason are prized above all else as the things that are reliable. But actually, if you miss out people's ability to feel and their emotional aspects, you're asking people to solve some of the most complex problems that have ever been faced using only half of their abilities to do so. Evolution equipped us with these things - they are essential to how we function as human beings, as social animals. We have found that bringing that dimension back in increases people's problem-solving, it strengthens the relationships between groups, it makes them feel more empowered, they're more willing to do things, change things, be bolder. So those inner parts of the human are very important dimensions for addressing climate change."

– Morag Watson, climate change policy expert and co-founder of the Sustainability Leadership Network

1.3.2 Compassion

"Compassion has an enormously practical application in the world. It is an entry point to action on all types of social and environmental issues."

– Tom Rivett-Carnac, political lobbyist for the UNFCCC and co-author of *The Future We Choose: Surviving the Climate Crisis*

Central to humanity's adaptive prosociality is the innate capacity for compassion. Compassion's profound evolutionary value has been to connect us with others and to impel social action - it helped us to survive and thrive as hunter-gatherers, contributes to the glue that holds more complex societies together, and has been a driving inspiration for countless reformers and visionary leaders.[123] At the current time it is crucial in energising appropriate response to environmental destruction and the suffering of those worst affected.

Like mindfulness, compassion is considered a 'compound construct', combining a number of tendencies, skills and qualities.[124] Scientists call it a 'motivational system' because it's not just a feeling but a complex component of psychology that shapes thoughts, physiological responses, intentions and ultimately behaviour. Definitions vary but most feature two basic processes: turning attention towards suffering, and feeling motivated to do something about it. Compassion shares with empathy the elements of understanding, resonance and desire to connect, however the two states are functionally and neurologically distinct.[125] While empathy – the sharing of another's emotion – can be distressing and contribute to burnout, compassion is a nourishing quality. Thus having compassion supports us to stay connected to the suffering of others rather than recoiling or shutting down.* Some experts suggest that compassion can manifest in different ways, contrasting a receptive and tender form with a 'fierce' form that is more proactive and robust - the spirit of a "momma bear" protecting her young, or the "caring force" associated with civil rights movements.[126]

Crucially, like mindfulness, our innate capacity for compassion can be developed through teaching and practise. Cultivating compassion has historically been an indispensable aspect of contemplative traditions. Today, a burgeoning range of interventions such as Compassion- Focussed Therapy, Mindful Self-Compassion and Mindfulness-Based Compassionate Living has been tailored for a secular context and subjected to rigorous randomised-controlled trials and meta-analyses.[128] These courses tend to introduce mindfulness as a necessary foundation and then go on to develop compassion through exercises that help us connect to the shared human condition, cultivate an attitude of care, and foster the intention to act appropriately in the face of distress. Exercises often focus inwards toward the self first, then include others and humanity as a whole. This approach is like exercising a muscle; gradually increasing the "weight" of the exercise as compassion grows stronger, widening the circle of identity, care and connection.

Compassion-based interventions are empirically linked to increases in health and wellbeing, prosocial behaviour, deeper feelings of intimacy and stronger pro-environmental values and behaviours, along with reduced aggressiveness, antisocial behaviour and in-group/out-group differentiations.[129] Recent research has also found that care and compassion elements are vital to many of the prosocial benefits of mindfulness courses described in this report.[130] While courses usually treat these elements as implicit qualities to be transmitted or embodied by the teacher, this finding suggests that care and compassion should be taught explicitly wherever possible.

*While within caring and humanitarian work it has become common to talk about 'compassion fatigue', a more accurate term might be empathic burnout. In contrast to compassion which can be a nourishing quality, sharing the distress of others for prolonged periods can lead to emotional exhaustion. The complex factors contributing to this condition often include undermining of the healthy working conditions that allow compassion to arise, and a lack of emphasis on self-care.[127]

Compassion for others and self-compassion are not significantly correlated in cross-sectional studies.[131] People often demonstrate one without the other and may need therefore to cultivate both in order to balance the desire to help others with the personal resource and resilience required to do so. As discussed further in Section 2.1.1, self-compassion helps us to acknowledge our own suffering without being overwhelmed and to manage difficult feelings like shame and guilt, which can trigger psychological defence mechanisms and impede positive engagement.[132] As climate tragedies worsen, development of both capacities is vital in helping us turn towards other human and non-human beings in their vulnerability and distress. Compassion is an antithesis to the fragmentation that both feeds the climate crisis and depresses collective response.

BOX 6: EXPLORE FURTHER

Compassion Training Courses

Evidence-based mindfulness courses have evolved over more than 40 years and tend to use Jon Kabat-Zinn's MBSR curriculum as a key reference point. By contrast, compassion-based training is a much newer area of innovation, without an obvious original course for the field to cohere around.

However, at least six empirically supported compassion-based interventions have been subject to rigorous testing through randomized controlled trials (RCTs).[133] Programmes vary in length but, like in-person mindfulness training, a typical compassion-based course includes weekly group sessions over a 6-12 week period and an element of daily home practice. Although the components of courses vary depending on their context, most include elements of mindfulness practice, prosocial affect meditations, exercises involving imagery, and education on the meaning and mechanisms of compassion and/or self-compassion.

What the research tells us
Meta-analyses of compassion-based interventions have found positive effects on participants' levels of compassion and self-compassion, mental health and emotion regulation, and interpersonal and social relationships.[134] Like mindfulness, the studies examining compassion training have so far tended to focus on individual benefits. However, a meta-analysis of studies examining compassion and similar 'loving kindness' meditations found robust increases in observable (e.g. facial expressions, real-world helping behaviour) and self-reported prosocial outcomes.[135] There is also increasing interest in evolving compassion courses to better target prosocial behaviours through a more relational approach.[136] Particularly when combined with sustainability education and a firm foundation of mindfulness practice, these innovations have great promise in strengthening the ability of individuals to recognise the suffering of others and of the natural world, develop the will to alleviate it and act accordingly.

"Compassion goes with mindfulness, because once we become aware of what's happening inside of us - all the feelings, the fears, the negative or manipulative thoughts - we need to have compassion for ourselves too. In short, mindfulness can help you become more compassionate, and compassion is necessary to stay mindful. If I don't balance the two, something is missing."

– Laureline Simon, Former UNFCCC Programme Officer & Founder of One Resilient Earth

2

Connection and the Climate Crisis

Connection and the Climate Crisis

"It's much easier to just talk about infrastructure and technical stuff. To really get people to understand the psychology is harder because they're not exempt, they would also have to look at themselves."

– Nadine Andrews, Climate Psychology Alliance member and Principal Social Researcher for the Scottish Government

This chapter addresses the functions of mindful and compassionate connection that are crucial in the particular context of the climate crisis; both in **mitigating** climate change and its felt **impacts**, and addressing the wider societal **conditions** that have brought it about. In reality these are never wholly separate propositions: human and planetary health are interlinked.[137] The neglected psychological impacts of the climate crisis tend to drive unsustainable behaviours that worsen the situation, both in terms of exploitative consumerism and in degrading our capacities for mutuality and collaboration when we need them most. However, by intervening in these mechanisms, it is possible to reverse these vicious cycles, with inner and outer conditions reinforcing each other in ways that are wholesome and generative.[138] Practices such as mindfulness and compassion do not merely soothe the inner symptoms of individuals beset by crisis, but support us to engage together in the difficult work of transforming unsustainable societal structures. In turn, healthier systemic conditions allow people to grow and flourish.

The chapter inquires first into perseverance, and the role of mindfulness and compassion in helping us to remain engaged at individual and collective levels with planetary disaster. We explore the implications of **turning towards distress** rather than shutting down, and developing the **resilience** necessary to cope in situations of profound difficulty. Connection with the crisis necessitates not only the management of negative impacts, but also the nourishment of positive emotion - and we discuss the relevance of mindfulness and compassion practices to **gratitude**, **hope** and **'positive emotional resonance'**.

Next, we explore the ways that the concept of (dis)connection pervades the mental models of self, others and world that drive the climate crisis and condition our responses to it. We examine the function of **worldview** – the inner lens through which we see the world and our **identity** within it; of **nature connection** – the extent to which people feel identified with the emergent phenomena of life; and of **polarisation** – escalating perception of others as inherently different and dangerous. Tracing the roots of the climate crisis through a culturally entrenched story of separateness, we ask how mindfulness, compassion and immersion in nature can support a more interconnected and survivable paradigm for the 21st Century.

Finally we turn to the unreliable mechanisms of **intentional action**, in acknowledgement that even radically enhanced engagement with and understanding of the climate crisis may not be sufficient to galvanise response. At the best of times, humanity's capacity for action in our individual and collective best interest is disrupted by forces both outside and within us. We explore the ways in which mindfulness and compassion can help us to realign intention with what the world needs, stay in touch with what matters to us most, and reconnect the disrupted circuitry of intention and action. In doing so they can help us to step out of undesirable behaviour patterns, supporting us to act consciously and creatively in the face of our greatest crisis.

2.1
Staying with the Trouble

"Mindfulness helps me to stay present to the most distressing aspects of my experience. To stay open-minded, accepting and flexible, rather than getting lost in anxiety... oscillating between past and future while the current possibilities for meaningful thinking, feeling and acting are inaccessible."

– Stephen Fitzpatrick, Director of Sustainability Communications, Culture and Wellbeing at Urgentem climate risk management

2.1.1 **Turning Towards the Difficult**

"Mindfulness has the potential not only to inspire us to protect the natural world, but also to equip us with the strength that we undoubtedly need to confront the true scale of the environmental crisis we face."

– Caroline Lucas, Member of the British Parliament, former UK Green Party leader and Member of the European Parliament

Climate change is a deeply uncomfortable reality to face. It calls upon us to dwell in stressful uncertainty, to witness the degradation of the natural world and to face the prospect of loss, deaths and the collapse of social order. We are not well adapted to cope with instability and threat of this magnitude, and responses range from outright denial and unrealistic optimism, to emotional repression and 'doomerism'.[139] Research clearly points to avoidance as a common defence strategy.[140] Besides inhibiting positive and timely engagement with the crisis, avoidance is no recipe for a healthy life - leading rather to chronic stress, depression, physical health problems and ultimately, greater anxiety.[141] Regardless of whether we feel directly threatened by the crisis, reckoning with the suffering of those in more vulnerable regions is painful and can similarly trigger avoidance. To stay with the trouble that we witness in order to respond requires depths of intention - and of personal and social resource.

The capacity for compassion is critical in facilitating engagement with the distressing truth of our current crisis. As discussed in Section 2.3.2, compassion includes both a willingness to turn towards suffering and also a sense of equanimity that enables one to do so sustainably. Cultivating this capacity, where we might otherwise experience empathic distress, reduces the likelihood that we will burn out or shut down. Some environmental activist groups emphasise the importance of inner activism - promoting e.g. forgiveness and compassion as an explicit component of their strategy. Recent campaigns have sought to avoid blaming messages while modelling the uncomfortable admission that "we are all part of the problem" as a basis for positive change.[142]

"Compassion brings forgiveness for oneself and others, to allow action from love rather than anger or hatred"

– Yanai Postelnik, Buddhist teacher and climate activist

Mindfulness teaching similarly emphasises the importance of 'turning towards' difficult experience. By treating discomfort as an object of enquiry, practitioners create a relationship of psychological distance from experiences that might otherwise be overwhelming. Becoming less identified with feelings paradoxically allows us to remain more connected with them. The possibility of feeling "comfortable with discomfort" radically expands our capacity for connecting with undesirable realities, as well as new and challenging information.[143] For instance, mindfulness training has been shown to reduce the sunk-cost bias - the tendency to continue investing resources in a failing endeavour, to avoid the pain of admitting that the initial investment is lost.[144] Instead, willingness to feel difficult emotions supports engagement with the problem and better decision-making.

The practice of reconnecting with difficulty is included in common training such as MBSR and MBCT, not only to increase tolerance, but also to generate insight and agency around the sources and mechanisms of distress. For example, MBCT encourages examination of ruminative thought and its relationship with depression, so as to intervene in relapse patterns.[145]

Importantly, a new wave of social mindfulness interventions treats distress not only as internal but as a collective phenomenon, promoting both insight into the pathologies reflected in public structures and institutions, and the will and capacity to reshape these to better meet societal needs (see Box 4).[146]

BOX 7: CASE STUDY
Joanna Macy and The Work That Reconnects

Mainstream sustainability discourse has only recently begun to recognise the inner dimension of the climate crisis, characterised by disconnection. However, some practitioners and pioneers have spent decades exploring this issue and developing interventions that can help participants develop a sense of interconnection.[147] Chief amongst these is Joanna Macy, a scholar of systems theory, who in the 1970's began to develop a visionary approach to social change based upon deep understanding of interdependencies.[148]

According to Macy, experiencing our interconnection allows us to develop awareness of our 'deep ecology' and realise the potential we have to make a difference in the world, which in turn engages us in appropriate behavioural response to the realities we face.[149] She developed these ideas into a programme called *The Work That Reconnects*, popularised through books including *Coming Back to Life* and *Active Hope*. Based on this work, experiential workshops and courses have been delivered to many thousands of people for several decades.[150] The programme's four stages resonate with many of the principles in this report. Participants engage in mindfulness- and compassion- informed practices to resource themselves before turning towards the fear and pain associated with global realities, developing the ability to 'see with new eyes' the interconnection of all phenomena before mobilising practical applications through relevant action.

Empirical testing of the programme is still in its early stages, but pilot studies have shown it to be engaging and popular.[151] More recently the meditation-based six week programme *Integrated Action* has further integrated mindfulness and compassion-based approaches with Macy's frameworks.

"One of the reasons that we're in this crisis is that people don't even have the time, or perhaps the courage, to feel what we're doing to nature and the climate and our planetary home. Unless one can make that connection then, in a sense, it's hard to find the resourcefulness to try to change things, and you're part of the problem."

– Caroline Lucas, Member of the British Parliament, former UK Green Party leader and Member of the European Parliament

2.1.2 **Psychological Resilience**

"The first ability that we should cultivate to support climate action is the ability to connect... to our own bodies, to others, to nature around us... But what emotions then come can be unpredictable, so the second ability would be to feel them without shutting down or recreating the distance"

– Laureline Simon, Former UNFCC Programme Officer and Founder of One Resilient Earth.

As ecological awareness grows, so do climate-grief, eco-anxiety and related depression, especially amongst the young.[152] Of all the inner dimensions of the climate crisis, it is the impact upon citizens' mental health that policy makers are most likely aware of.[153] Difficult emotions like grief and anxiety are often appropriate and potentially motivating responses to the climate crisis - conducive to "honouring our pain for the world" as described by Joanna Macy (see Box 7)[154]. However, without sufficient psychological resilience, social support and a sense of progress towards climate goals they can become deeply distressing, paralysing and counter-productive. A vicious cycle can emerge in which climate change impacts mental health, which in turn increases unsustainable behaviours and reduces civic engagement, limiting climate action and worsening future impacts.[155] For instance, chronic stress leads to reduced prosociality, in turn promoting both overconsumption and social isolation.

Psychological resilience is therefore a crucial concept for understanding climate impacts and potential solutions. While superficially, the idea might suggest 'a stiff upper lip' or 'bouncing back' from adversity, real resilience specifically entails a creative and adaptive response to change, rather than resisting or ignoring it.[156] Resilience is important at a population level to interrupt the vicious cycle between mind and climate change, and support societal adaptation in the face of worsening climate disruption.[157] It is also crucial for professionals and activists engaged with climate issues on a daily basis. Enacting connection and care whilst grappling with social structures shaped by disconnection and "uncare" can be painful and exhausting. Indeed, this is a particular challenge reported in support groups for climate workers and youth activists.

Mindfulness and self-compassion practices are known to increase resilience.[158] They help to regulate difficult emotions like fear, anger and sadness and integrate them healthily.[159] Mindfulness in particular supports the inner stability that permits engagement with turbulent conditions. For example, improved ability to sense potential overwhelm allows one to redirect attention to self-care and self-soothing elements of practice, before potentially turning towards difficult concepts once again when sufficiently steady and restored.

Self-compassion can support practitioners to stay connected with the content of their internal world, rather than living in flight from difficult thoughts and emotions - particularly helping to regulate guilt, shame and self-criticism.[160] Although shame can be a powerful driver of change when held with care and forgiveness, painful self-judgement can have the opposite effect, entrenching unhelpful views and behaviour.[161] Training emphasises self-acceptance, explicitly including personal weaknesses, and the acknowledgement of negative experiences.

The reduction of anxiety, stress and depression are among the most consistent mindfulness research findings over the last 40 years.[162] Mindfulness has also been shown to increase 'cognitive resilience' by protecting mental functions from degradation, depletion, or failure in the face of substantial stressors.[163] In particular, mindfulness can protect and enhance 'working memory',[164] the brain system that stores and manipulates information in complex cognitive tasks like decision-making, communicating and guiding behaviour. High stress depletes working memory, leading to distraction, poor mood, psychological disorders, and performance errors.[165] As well as facilitating continued connection through resilience therefore, mindfulness practice has the potential to contribute to a necessary cognitive foundation for effective and sustainable climate action and help mitigate burnout.[166]

"Mindfulness makes me a better politician by helping me not get carried away by all the emotions, stress and egoic behaviour of politics. By taking a bit more distance and seeing how relative these things are, you can better connect with people and have better success."

– Petra De Sutter, Deputy Prime Minister of Belgium

2.1.3 Positive emotion and engagement

"Living and working under the weight of the climate emergency depletes people, inside as well as out. If we're not going to burn out, we need to stay connected with those elements like joy, hope and nature that keep restoring our energy for the work."

– Katie White OBE, Executive Director Advocacy and Campaigns, WWF

Coping amid the realities of climate change entails more than the management of difficult emotions. The inner nourishment that fosters resilience comes from connection with a complementary sphere of positive feeling that encompasses, among other things, gratitude, hope and love. Activating our rich resource of positive affect is crucial not only in mitigating overwhelm but in finding the motivation to engage with the hard work and sacrifice called upon by the crisis.

In addition to supporting recovery from stress,[167] positive emotions can broaden and build our perceptual and cognitive capabilities. During positive emotional experiences awareness is expanded, enabling people to connect distant ideas and act creatively, flexibly, and with a sense of connection to the future.[168] Happiness and subjective wellbeing are also linked to social engagement and sustainable behaviour.[169] Furthermore, evidence shows that positive emotions are contagious,[170] and that our capacity for 'positive emotional resonance' is central to human relational bonds and collaboration. The collective dimension of positive emotion is critical in motivating climate action - thought leaders increasingly suggest that inspiring latent public engagement is best approached by enabling people to connect emotionally with a sense of great, shared endeavour.[171]

Some approaches point to **gratitude** as an important emotion in sustaining climate engagement (see Box 7). This nourishing feeling helps us to stay connected with what we appreciate in life, and is associated with life satisfaction.[172] But experts also consider it part of the inner 'care system' activating prosocial emotions and behaviour by reminding us of things we care *about*. [173] Throughout social evolution, this 'self-transcendent' emotion helped us solve problems relating to caretaking and cooperation.[174]

Others emphasise '**active hope**' or 'stubborn optimism', as a crucial quality for meeting the climate crisis.[175] For example, senior policymakers have said that optimism was not the outcome of success in Paris but the cause of it, creating a sense of positive momentum that propelled negotiations. Importantly, in contrast to blind faith in a positive outcome, this stance is characterised by a "fierce conviction that no matter how difficult, we must and we can rise to the challenge".[176]

Their role in activating positive emotions highlights both mindfulness and compassion practices as key inner components of climate action. The robust clinical evidence base for mindfulness training has led to its popular association with managing negative emotions.[177] However it likewise helps activate the positive feeling that can inspire engagement and perseverance.[178] Mindfulness is also implicated in strengthening *awareness* of positive emotions.[179] Research links both mindfulness and compassion to positive affect,[180] and compassion has been shown to foster positive feeling even in the face of significant distress.[181] Increased positive affect also accounts for much of the impact mindfulness has on life satisfaction.[182]

In particular, mindfulness is a factor in cultivating gratitude: even the most basic understanding of mindfulness tends to include the related quality of appreciation. This can be both an outcome of present moment awareness and a motivating factor[183] - cultivating everyday wonder is a common gateway to practise. Accordingly, research links dispositional mindfulness with higher gratitude.[184] In view of substantial evidence from positive psychology, mindfulness-based interventions increasingly include explicit gratitude practices.

Meanwhile, hope-based therapeutic modalities often include meditation elements, in part because attention regulation and reduction in stress helps create conditions for hope to arise. Pilot studies have found that mindfulness training can lead to an increased sense of hope.[185,186] In the workplace, mindfulness has been found to develop 'psychological capital', a construct that includes hope, optimism, resilience, and a sense of personal agency.[187]

2.2
Joined-up World

"The most remarkable feature of this historical moment on Earth, is not that we are on the way to destroying the world — we've actually been on the way for quite a while. It is that we are beginning to wake up, as from a millennia-long sleep, to a whole new relationship to our world, to ourselves and each other."

– Joanna Macy, author, activist and scholar of general systems theory and deep ecology

2.2.1 Holistic Worldview and Expanded Identity

"The Anthropocene is characterised by a certain perceptual blindness. People are insensitive to the connections between their actions and global ecosystems."

– Polina Chebotareva, *Connectedness: An Encyclopaedia of the Anthropocene*

In the context of climate change, most technical solutions are what sustainability scientists might call 'shallow leverage points' - places in a system where intervention is relatively accessible but minimally influential, akin to treating symptoms of a disease. By contrast, intervention at deeper leverage points may be more difficult but potentially far more transformative.[188] At perhaps the deepest level, the human behaviours driving climate change are founded upon a culturally conditioned **worldview** characterised by separation of ourselves from others and from nature.[189] Our sense of fundamental independence both drives and validates our exploitation of the world. It also underpins the widespread helplessness that individuals feel regarding climate change. What can one lone person do in the face of such a leviathan threat? Blind to the consequences of our actions at scale we likewise neglect our collective power and responsibility to bring about positive change. The potential to address individual and collective worldviews thus represents a deep leverage point for climate action.[190]

Our worldview may be understood as an internal map, or the lens through which we see to navigate life. It is usually heavily influenced by a foundational story or image that accounts for humanity's place in the world, and acts as a blueprint for social norms. Entangled within this cultural code is our story of **identity**; what it means to be 'me' or 'us'. Identity integrates aspects of both inner life and the social world. It may refer narrowly to one's own mind or body, or more broadly towards larger groups - for example, a family, tribe, nation, civilisation, species, or all life on earth. Radical differences in cultural behaviour emerge depending on the connectedness inherent in worldview and identity. For example, whereas historically some civilizations have imagined themselves enmeshed within a harmonic "web of life", others have come to picture humanity alone at the top of a pyramid of power.[191]

Western history has deep roots in this prevailing story of human dominion over nature - and a related sense of identity as primarily located within the individual, competing with others for success (see also Section 1.3.1). But practices such as compassion and mindfulness can help us to nurture an understanding of the world as inherently connected, and identity as founded on relationship. The pioneering mindfulness teacher Thich Nat Han described this worldview as one of *inter-being*.[192] Its importance to sustainability cannot be overemphasised: those who identify with others and with nature are more likely to protect their 'expanded self'.[193]

For example, along with gratitude and awe, compassion is considered to be a 'self-transcendent emotion': one that moves people to look beyond their own needs and desires to focus on others, strengthening social connection. Others use the term "self-expanding" to describe the way that such emotions can broaden the sense of identity beyond a narrowly constructed 'self'.[194] In this sense cultivating compassion not only expands the circle of care to include others, but subtly expands the self to include others. This insight into inter-being has prompted some researchers to include an aspect of wisdom in their definition of compassion.

The cultivation of metacognition through mindfulness practice can help us to see how we are constructing our identity from moment to moment. If our intention is towards a wider, more connected view, we may choose to direct awareness towards the interdependencies that surround and support our life on earth. This practice is an essential element in Indigenous teachings and contemplative traditions and is increasingly supported by modern science, promoting systemic understanding of ourselves, others and world as 'intra-connected'.[195]

More generally, mindfulness is associated with a more egalitarian outlook and reduced perception of dominance hierarchies, and mindful curiosity is associated with less defensiveness when worldviews are challenged.[196] Mindfulness and compassion are also linked with increased understanding of nature-connectedness, a less competitive mindset, a systems-level understanding that human activities cause climate change, and an associated appetite for policy changes.[197] Furthermore as discussed in Section 2.3.1, mindfulness and compassion can be influential in activating particular sets of values.

Worldviews do not change simply because we decide they should, and setting out to dismantle belief systems can have the result of strengthening them. When something so closely bound with our identity is challenged we often defend ourselves by doubling down.[198] Conversely, the ability to gain distance from thoughts and emotions can allow us to interrogate our own beliefs.[199] Thus with an appropriately wide framing, social or ecological mindfulness interventions could support us to examine and challenge internalised cultural messages of separation and superiority (see Box 4).[200] Perhaps more importantly, a committed, long-term mindfulness practice may directly support a 'joined-up' experience of the world, by habituating the holistic-intuitive mode of mind that processes perception in terms of the whole, and of relationships between integrated parts (see Box 8).[201]

"Mindfulness and compassion help you to understand that we are all connected. At the same time, they also help you to act effectively. So, at one level, mindfulness can be a tool, it gives you a bit more capacity to get things done - and then gradually might come this understanding of interdependency."

– Yoko Alendar, Member of the Estonian Parliament and chair of its Environment Committee

Holistic-Intuitive Cognition

Cognitive scientists identify two distinct 'modes' of mind that are responsible for radically different ways of attending to the world.[202] 'Holistic-intuitive' describes a primal mode of understanding in which the mind seeks out patterns in the environment and updates its working models of reality intuitively. This open and receptive mode comprehends relatedness and enables us to perceive the world as a coherent, connected whole. Modern humans - particularly in the West - have however come to be dominated by a second way of knowing based on abstract, self-contained mental concepts moulded by our historical privileging of logical processing.[203] In this 'verbal-conceptual mode', the world is boiled down to a collection of abstract rules and pieces; the discrete symbolic objects that serve goal-driven problem-solving. In this mode we process the world in inanimate "chunks", oblivious to the whole system in which we act.[204] We model the world as complicated, not complex - and we attend to dissociated parts, rather than the whole. Psychiatrist and author Iain Mcgilchrist proposes that this mode of mind evolved to help humans to exploit the world rather than understand it.[205]

Practising mindfulness can bring an intentional shift, or re-balancing between these modes of mind. Practitioners are encouraged to notice the limitations of 'driven doing' (goal-focused, verbal-conceptual) mode, nurture the conditions for holistic-intuitive awareness, and learn to balance the two. Mindful awareness does not reject verbal-conceptual processing but rather includes it within a holistic map. Practitioners learn to integrate thinking into an intuitive, embodied experience of the world as interconnected and alive – a mode of understanding more conductive to sustainability than the reductive computational model elevated by Western thought in recent centuries.[206]

"Mindfulness has become a tool to make people more effective or achieve better mental health. But mindfulness also develops insight, and through insight you can change your mental structures and thereby your perception of the world. I think if more people get interested in the way that their worldview is constructed, it will only be good for humanity's collective ability to deal with our crises."

- Tom Rivett-Carnac, political lobbyist for the UNFCCC and co-author of *The Future We Choose: Surviving the Climate Crisis*

2.2.2 **Resisting Polarisation**

"It will take all of us working together, pushing and pulling each other with honesty and with respect, to accelerate the urgent solutions. Outrage and optimism both have roles to play.

As we put our muskets down, we will realise that more than blame or punishment, we must restore the depletion, in ourselves as well as in the natural world. Underneath the grief and the anger, we harbour a hunger for healing."

– Christiana Figueres, Former Executive Secretary of the UNFCCC and co-author of *The Future We Choose: Surviving the Climate Crisis*

Over and beyond an individualised worldview, the disconnect that we perceive between 'people like us' and others is widening. Not only is public opinion diverging but we are now more likely than ever to distrust and dislike those with differing opinions - to exhibit 'affective polarisation'.[207] Research suggests that contemporary hyperpolarisation is driven by an interaction between social media and human confirmation bias.[208] Our innate tendency to hear what we want to hear is amplified by personalised digital media diets, creating a 'filter bubble' that serves us information that confirms our existing beliefs, to the exclusion - even demonisation - of conflicting views. Society thus becomes fractured into opposing tribes, each wielding 'evidence' that their view is correct. In countries such as the US, extreme political polarisation is emerging as a result.[209]

Consequences for climate action are dire where tribal dynamics shape partisan attitudes to sustainability. Unfortunately, beliefs surrounding climate change are increasingly polarised, with camps forming along political divides - in part fuelled by vested interests' influence in party politics.[210] Even within climate activism, factions emerge whose escalating differences threaten to overcome their capacity to collaborate. Escaping these echo-chambers of selective information is crucial in re-establishing climate action as a cause beyond politics, and mustering the cooperation necessary to turn the rising tide.

Several benefits of practice already discussed point to mindfulness as a key tool in countering polarisation. For example, fight-flight mode can greatly escalate social conflict: noticing triggers and regulating threat response through mindfulness can help us to avoid perceiving disagreement as attack (see also section 2.3.3).[211] Furthermore, enhanced cognitive flexibility and perspective-taking can reduce confirmation bias, while increased receptivity and tolerance of discomfort allows us to remain open to challenging information.[212] While these advantages are noted as if they were separate, it's possible to see how each is a dimension of a single system that supports open-mindedness.

Studies have shown that both mindfulness practice and 'befriending meditation' similar to compassion practice directly reduce affective polarisation.[213] Unsurprisingly then, mindfulness training is shown to encourage prosocial behaviour across group boundaries, enabling constructive solutions to shared problems.[214]

"A lot of environmental NGOs deliberately trigger people because that's good for firing up your supporters or getting media hits or funding. But it comes at a high price: every time we trigger our members with upsetting imagery we are, in effect, causing a fight-flight-freeze reaction that then deepens political polarisation. And we cannot solve climate change if we're hyperpolarised."

– Alex Evans, author, founder of A Larger Us, former Campaign Director at Avaaz

2.2.3 **Nature Connection**

"We humans tend to think of ourselves as the most important species on the planet. Being so self-centred is the main reason we destroy the environment. The only sustainable solution will be to let go of this mindset, this costly illusion that we are outside of nature, even the rulers of nature. The capacities that enable you to let go of this illusion, to shift mindsets, are very much promoted by mindfulness and meditation."

– Esther Ouwehand, Member of the Dutch Parliament and leader of political party PvdD

Our deep-running human story of dominance and disconnection is entrenched by widespread isolation from nature, both physical and emotional. Life increasingly mediated by urban environments and technology lacks the experience of and engagement with nature that fosters familiarity and identification with the living world. Meanwhile culture teaches us to objectify plants and animals as resources to be exploited. Scholars have thus begun to recognise the importance of reconnecting intellectually and emotionally with nature to support sustainability[215] - and many sustainability scholars and NGOs consider nature-connection as central to their evidence-based theories of change.[216]

Nature connection has benefits to individual mental and physical health, and individuals with high nature-connectedness - a sense of close relationship with nature - have been found to be roughly twice as likely to exhibit pro-environmental and conservation behaviours.[217] Furthermore, evidence shows that nature-connectedness stimulates caring, intrinsic values (see also Section 2.3.1) and is a stronger motivator of pro-environmental behaviours in children than knowledge of nature.[218]

Mindfulness practices align strongly with proposed pathways for enhancing nature connection such as sensory noticing of nature, appreciating natural beauty and cultivating compassion.[219] Indeed an early systematic study into pathways to nature connection suggest that it requires not only time spent in nature but crucially also the particular quality of engagement with natural surroundings that mindfulness can support.[220] The same study found that practising compassion and appreciation can promote deeper identification with nature, and emphasises the important role of emotional awareness in promoting meaningful connection.

Elsewhere, research demonstrates a mutually reinforcing relationship between mindfulness and nature connection: for example, contact with natural environments can help develop an effortless sense of presence and mindful non-evaluative attention, while mindfulness can allow people to engage with nature experiences more fully.[221] Other studies indicate that connection to nature and mindfulness can work synergistically to enhance psychological wellbeing and pro-social values.[222] This effect has been found in both remote, wilderness contexts and in urban settings.[223] In recent years, nature-based mindfulness offerings have multiplied, including mindful nature walks and mindful attention practices focused on ecological elements such as trees. These have in turn been shown to help people extend compassion to the wider environment.[224]

While all such evidence is to be welcomed, it must be tempered by the understanding that disconnection from nature is a problem embedded in societal inequalities. Access to unpolluted green open spaces is lower among many ethnic minority and low income communities living in urban areas, impacting mental and physical health.[225] For nature-based mindfulness offerings to become a meaningful part of climate policy efforts, providing more equitable access to nature must become a key priority.

"I think what's needed is to understand the human being as a holistic thing... What is my body, my mind or my feelings? They cannot exist without this whole environment that I subsist in. There is no fish without water. There's no human without this planet. I am of this planet."

- John Doyle, Sustainable Development Policy Coordinator of the European Commission, Information Society and Media Directorate-General

2.3
Intention and Action

"IPCC reports, going back to 1990, have not been heeded. Where is the report on that? Because that's the one we really need. Where is the report with IPCC-level rigour and authority that explains the gap between what we know and what we do at scale?"

– Jonathan Rowson, Director of Perspectiva, former Director of the RSA's Social Brain Centre

2.3.1 Wiser Wanting

Increasingly widespread knowledge about the climate emergency has not translated into sustainable behaviour and action on a mass scale.[226] This pressing issue however reflects an enduring set of human problems: most of the time there are several weak links in the causal chain between what we know and what we do.[227]

Firstly, at individual and societal levels we are not always inclined to want what is actually good for us. Much like threat response, the things that we reach for with the greatest immediacy in our lives are often governed by outdated adaptive triggers - for example the drive to eat all that we can find of a tasty food when it is available. Our consumer economy operates the same unexamined more-is-better principal that once drove us to lay down fat for times of scarcity.

Public awareness is growing around the deep cost of consumer culture:[228] the environmental 'externalities' that are not factored into economics or paid for by polluters - typically impacting vulnerable regions and communities far more severely than those of us who over-consume.[229] Less visible perhaps is the failure of this system on its own terms. The satisfaction gained from consuming goods or services, described by economists as 'utility', is held up as the ultimate good. However, colossal growth in economic activity and consumer spending in post-industrial nations over the last 70 years has not led overall to increased life satisfaction, or at least any gains have been offset by drag factors like overwork, inequality, degradation of social trust and mental health problems.[230] By prioritising spending power to the exclusion of other types of wealth, we become disconnected from inner sources of happiness and from a realistic sense of what - and how much - we materially need in order to live a satisfying and comfortable life.

Both mindfulness and compassion practice have potential to shift this relationship with material appetites.[231] Not only can openness and curiosity contribute to awareness around types of consumption and relationships such as supply chains, but connection to inner experience can also lead to direct insight into how distress and happiness arise. Practitioners may thus cultivate a more acute understanding of their needs - and the limits of those needs. Furthermore, rather than limiting inquiry to the individual as clinical applications have thus far, **social mindfulness** interventions explicitly address structural and cultural patterns in society (see Box 4).[232] This ongoing wave of innovation is particularly important in linking personal practice to broader systemic change.

Importantly, mindfulness and compassion training both emphasise a deliberate shift in intention. In the case of mindfulness, practice is inclined towards patience, acceptance and appreciation of the present moment. These qualities canreconnect us consciously with what we already have, potentially reducing the magnetism of 'more'.[233] Compassion practices refocus priorities around care, helping and personal relationships over self-interest.[234] As well as increasing pro-social attitudes, these qualities have been shown to inhibit conflicting motivators such as the competitive and individualistic mindset associated with unsustainable consumption.[235]

Developing insight into sources of happiness and feeling the benefit of living with intentions like appreciation and care can, over time, lead to more lasting changes in values - our guiding principles or the things that matter to us most. Accordingly, studies show that cultivating mindfulness and compassion strengthens **intrinsic values** - ends that are inherently rewarding to pursue, such as bonds with friends and family, nature-connection, self-acceptance and concern for others.[236] Intrinsic values are associated with increased happiness and more sustainable behaviour, in contrast to extrinsic values such as external approval, wealth and material success, which are associated with lower satisfaction (see also Section 2.3.3).[237] Hence, mindfulness and compassion training show potential to support a shift to less resource-intensive lifestyles.[238]

While the collective power of consumers should not be underestimated, it must be acknowledged that individuals are not the ultimate locus of power when it comes to sustainable consumption. Vast, impersonal financial systems are founded on manipulation and growth of consumer culture, and many powerful interests resist environmental protections wholesale wherever their bottom line is threatened. Nonetheless we must ask what are the inner conditions that maintain acceptance of these conditions at a global scale, and what we might do to counter mass apathy in the face of exploitation. From raising awareness and marshalling collective leverage to holding Government and corporations accountable, inner capacities like mindfulness and compassion underpin our shared agency to bring about transformation.[239]

"We have the climate crisis because of our inner crisis. Our minds are focussed on materialism, consumerism, production, economic growth. Inner discontent is reflected outside in our greed; endless pursuit of material possessions. Even if we don't need them, we go on producing them and selling them and buying them and holding them."

–Satish Kumar, author, founder of Schumacher College, and Editor-in-Chief of Resurgence and Ecologist magazines

2.3.2 The Inner Compass

"Mindfulness really enables me to stay in touch with what is most important to me: my own values."

– Esther Ouwehand, Member of the Dutch Parliament and leader of political party PvdD

Research shows that values influence how we interpret and respond to facts, including those about climate change.[240] However while values may be important to motivation, not all of our values are influential at all times. They tend to be temporarily 'engaged' by certain experiences or through conscious effort. Furthermore our values need not be consistent: rather contradictory values can inhibit one another, so that when one value set is engaged, another may be suppressed.[241] For example, personal freedom might be important to us but there will be circumstances where we instead conform to social norms because we also value justice and community. Intrinsic and extrinsic values are two such mutually inhibiting sets. Studies indicate that 75% of people consider their own behaviour to be led by intrinsic values, but a similar proportion believe that extrinsic values are primary for most other people.[242] The good news, we might conclude, is that mostly we at least aspire to prioritise connection and care, and tend to underestimate others in this regard. *I care, but everyone else is out for himself.* On the other hand, this aspiration does not always translate into intrinsic motivation that is perceptible to others, signalling that we may be struggling at a cultural level to live in alignment with what we value.

Powerful momentum maintains the status quo of our extrinsically dominated society. Cultural norms prioritising wealth and status, social priming through media and marketing, and the inertia of our own habits all contribute to conditions that engage extrinsic values and suppress the intrinsic, perpetuating unsustainable behaviour. Whatever the prevailing cultural current, the default is to be swept along, becoming disconnected from our own sense of what is most important. Knowing what really matters to us in these adverse conditions requires a powerful attunement to our values - the inner compass that shows true north amid competing influences.

Mindfulness and compassion practices support reconnection with this inner compass in important ways. By habitually setting aside space for inner reflection we can come more closely to know our own minds and hearts, and strengthen relationship with our own better judgement. Mindfulness of the body is a particularly important conduit of our deepest values. The body supplies an endless stream of subtle signals that support our understanding of the world and ethical engagement with it – the nagging feeling in the gut, for example, that tells us we're going along with an action that we don't agree with. Reconnecting with this innate, embodied discernment can take time, but with patience and practise it is an invaluable source of insight. As discussed in Section 1.2.1, mindfulness training can rebuild this connection with the body, helping practitioners develop greater depths of intuition and supporting personal integrity.

Indeed evidence shows that the mental health benefit of mindfulness results in part from individuals' improved recognition of what they truly value and find meaningful.[243] Certain mindfulness-informed interventions are founded specifically upon this quality of access to values. For example, Acceptance & Commitment Therapy (ACT) combats health issues by helping participants develop a life that feels more rich and satisfying *according to their own standards*.[244] In the context of sustainability, mindfulness has also been shown to stimulate deeper reflection on what matters to us, and our own behaviour as consumers.[245]

"I don't just use mindfulness to manage stress, but to create a connection within this work to something deeper. I think of mindfulness as something that connects me with the web of life on our planet; that could reconnect us all. Something that could help the planet prosper – not financially, but in terms of abundance for all living things. For me, it's about a deep connection."

- Alviina Alametsä, Member of the European Parliament serving on the Committee on Foreign Affairs

BOX 9:

Does mindfulness support sustainable behaviour?

For 20 years, researchers have investigated whether mindfulness promotes pro-environmental behaviours (PEB), which are habits that "harm the environment as little as possible, or even benefit the environment".[246]

Much of this research focuses on the positive relationship between PEB and 'trait mindfulness', which is a person's baseline or average level of mindfulness.[247] Studies show that those with higher levels of trait mindfulness tend to consume more sustainably, eat less meat, and participate more in environmental activism.[248] Individuals who follow an active mindfulness practice, such as meditation or other mind-body exercises, were found to perform more PEB and have a lower environmental impact associated with their diet.[249]

Given that mindfulness practice increases trait mindfulness, recent research has enquired into whether mindfulness training could underpin interventions to motivate sustainable behaviour.[250] Based on related studies, researchers hypothesise that mindfulness-induced improvements in PEB take at least one year of regular practice.[251] The impact of mindfulness practice on PEB is thought to arise mainly from intermediate changes in individuals' self-regulation,[252] pro-sociality,[253] feelings of nature-connectedness,[254] materialism,[255] intrinsic values,[256] subjective well-being,[257] and health-related behaviour changes.[258]

2.3.3 Intentional Response

"Between stimulus and response there is a space. In that space is our power to choose our response. In our response lies our growth and our freedom."

– Viktor Frankl, paraphrased by Stephen Covey

Values are influential in shaping our beliefs, attitudes and intentions, but they are not sufficient in themselves to direct our behaviour. As sustainability researchers have long been aware, a disconnect persists between values and behaviour; commonly described as the "value-action gap". Research confirms a widespread tendency to report pro-environmental attitudes and support for sustainability policies without prioritising sustainable consumption behaviours.[259]

Even when we are quite clear about what it is we want, we aren't always in control of our behaviour as we might imagine. Our society is built upon a model of humans as rational agents, acting out of choice. But neuro- and cognitive science increasingly reveal these assumptions to be in error (see also Section 1.1.2).[260] Throughout life, intentions compete with involuntary impulses and entrenched habits when it comes to directing behaviour. They often lose - which is why we find it so difficult to change harmful patterns.[261]

Beyond the sphere of sustainability, we are all too familiar with the actions that reflect neither our intentions nor our character. We blurt out a hurtful comment. Panic-buy toilet paper. This type of behaviour belongs to the category of **'reactivity'** - impulsive functioning prompted by transitory emotion like anger or fear, bypassing good sense.[262] Automatic behaviour is not limited to the heat of the moment. Studies confirm that we spend a large portion of our daily lives carrying out actions whilst our minds are wandering in thought - a state known as the 'default mode' and more commonly as 'autopilot'.[263] In this mode, our conscious experience is disconnected both from the outer world - including others and nature - and from our own values and intentions for change. These forces too have acquired a digital dimension. While some applications of digital technology may support behaviour change, many more make it harder, keeping us locked into the 'dark flow' of automatic behaviour through mechanisms like 'infinite' scrolling.[264] Living on autopilot, we are more likely to react blindly to experience, in contrast to the creative **responsiveness** that becomes possible when we are in touch with our inner world, and can connect intention to conscious choice.

A central component of mindfulness training focuses upon this distinction between reaction and response, and upon restoring intention as the driver of our actions. Practitioners become familiar with the 'mindful pause': interrupting the flow of action to check in with present moment experience, and restoring awareness to interconnected intention, action and potential outcomes.[265] Over time, they can also learn to spot habits of automatic thought and behaviour, and to acknowledge impulses without reacting.

Interrupting autopilot is a proven factor in the clinical effectiveness of mindfulness-based interventions, and many applications relate to automatic behaviours such as automatic eating, aspects of alcoholism and ruminative thinking that can lead to depressive relapse.[266] Several studies link trait mindfulness to lower levels of reactivity and impulsivity.[267] Early research now shows that mindfulness training with a sustainability focus helps practitioners to intervene in unconscious, unsustainable consumption routines.[268] The common denominator of these proven applications is restored intention: mindfulness can help people to resist involuntary impulses and consciously reconnect behaviour with deeper motivations.

Accordingly, mindfulness interventions have been shown to develop the tendency towards 'autonomous motivation': intentionally engaging in behaviour because it is perceived to be consistent with our intrinsic goals.[269] Behavioural evidence likewise shows that mindfulness-informed Acceptance and Commitment Therapy (ACT) can boost participants' ability to act in values-consistent ways.[270] More specifically, research now supports the view that mindfulness practice can help to reduce the value-action gap in the context of sustainable consumption.[271] Such outcomes suggest promising approaches to key drivers of climate change. At several precarious junctions, mindfulness and compassion could help to strengthen critical links between knowledge of our predicament and appropriate response - reorienting intention towards what the world needs and fostering the inner conditions for appropriate, purposeful action.

BOX 10: CASE STUDY

European Union Climate Leaders Programme

BEYOND is a Climate & Environmental Leadership Programme, from the Awaris Inner Green Deal Initiative. It aims to drive sustainability from within by supporting decision makers to cultivate mindfulness and compassion, develop new habits and collaborate with a common purpose.

100 leaders from the EU - including 40 from the European Parliament, Council and Commision - took part in the pilot programme, exploring both the inner dimension of sustainability in terms of mindfulness, compassion, values and beliefs, and outer aspects such as behaviour change, collaboration and workplace initiatives.

A pilot study was conducted in 2021/22.[272] According to preliminary findings, participants demonstrated:

- significant increase in nature connectedness;

- significant increase in climate agency (e.g. voting for environmental parties, signing petitions) and adaptation behaviour (taking measures to prepare for climate impacts);

- clear links between compassion and pro-environmental behaviour;

- increased integration of sustainability concerns into work, such as budget allocations, human resource allocation, internal working structures and stakeholder relationships;

- significant increase in well-being; and

- significant reduction in climate anxiety.

The programme has received widespread recognition. The EU's training Institute EUSA funded the development and launch of a new series of programmes for management across EU Institutions.

"Many of my political colleagues will think mindfulness is not really a natural science. But we have to think of it like that. We have to look at different ways to get to the next level of attitude, behaviour and systems change."

- Bas Eickhout, Member of the European Parliament and deputy chairman of the Greens–European Free Alliance, co-author of 2007 IPCC report

Conclusion

Conclusion

This report is dedicated to anyone - policy maker, professional or private citizen - who has watched with alarm the clock ticking down on climate change and wondered, "what are we missing?" Indeed, as groundbreaking research now clearly demonstrates, a critical dimension of the climate crisis has been excluded from the prevalent view. Climate change is a physical reality demanding political and practical solutions. But the wanting, co-creating, negotiating, and enacting of those solutions depends wholly upon **inner capacities** of the human mind and heart that have hitherto been absent from mainstream theories of change.

Against this background, this report makes the urgent case for more attention to, more research into, and more respect for individual and collective inner capacities as equal to material concerns in addressing climate-related systems change. In doing so it is congruent with the latest reporting from the IPCC, which explicitly references the role of "inner transformation towards sustainability."

Central to this inner dimension of climate response is comprehension of the damage wrought by a mindset of separateness - and cultivation of the human capacities that support radical reconnection with ourselves, with others and with nature. As such we have outlined the relationships of mindfulness and compassion to particular, interrelated faculties of connection, highlighting their foundational relevance to climate response at all levels. These applications are supported by theory and evidence that recommends mindfulness and compassion training as highly promising approaches to the neglected inner dimension of sustainability challenges. Where problems are considered in isolation, these approaches might be seen as interchangeable with other interventions - for example, prescription drugs are an accepted short-term alternative to working with difficult emotion through mindfulness practice. However, the benefit of mindfulness and compassion training in so many **simultaneous** aspects of this crisis heightens impetus for policymakers to step beyond restrictive silos and consider the range of benefit as an integrated whole. The widespread value of these inner capacities to both the individual and to society points furthermore to their **foundational** importance in human flourishing.

The inner capacities of citizens and leaders have been ignored for too long, and we must now start investing in them without further harmful delay. Policy recommendations follow therefore at the end of this report. Many insights offered here require further research, and further innovation is needed to propagate framing of mindfulness and compassion practices in a social and ecological context. However the pressing urgency of our circumstances dictates that we must now prioritise a whole-system approach to evidence-building and action in this area. To wait for meta-analyses of multiple randomised controlled trials in every insolated application repeats the outdated, siloed thinking that sidelines these foundational capacities, overlooking their value at a system level. Strong evidence for mindfulness and compassion training in supporting wellbeing, self-regulation, emotional intelligence, psychological resilience and healthy relationships is enough on its own terms to prompt widening of access in this time of profound disruption. However, these capacities should be understood not just as isolated interventions amid worsening climate impacts but as fundamental in addressing the root causes of climate change, and the worldviews and behaviours that drive it.

We do not propose that attending to inner capacities is enough to solve the crisis – only that if we do not, solutions will likely continue to elude us. Beyond the essential tools of policy and technology, we must galvanise the public and political capacity to do the work that lies ahead. Whether we seek to understand the source of the problem, to shift the behaviours that drive it or to nurture the courage and community that we will need as stewards of an uncertain future, mindfulness and compassion can form an essential foundation. In nurturing these inner capacities we may discover the 'beautiful coincidence' that the pathways to robust climate action and to individual and collective wellbeing are one and the same.

Policy Recommendations

1. Policy integration and mainstreaming

Considerations of the inner dimensions of climate change - its human cultural, psychological, emotional, and neurophysiological aspects - are largely absent in mainstream climate policy and policymaking approaches. Governments, public institutions and NGOs should consider the role of trainable inner capacities, such as mindfulness and compassion, in their development and implementation of public policy. In particular:

- As per mainstreaming of other issues such as gender equality, consideration of inner human capacities should be incorporated into policy thinking through systematic integration - modifying existing processes and structures at all levels and across all sectors of society.

- Agencies working on climate action should include inner human capacities in their theories of change, and raise awareness about their importance within the sectors that they interact with. As an example, the United Nations Development Programme has established the Conscious Food Systems Alliance (CoFSA) to develop initiatives that address mindsets and promote inner capacities, including mindfulness and compassion, amongst those working in the global food & agriculture system, in order to increase its equity and sustainability.

- Governments should establish central expertise for mainstreaming inner dimensions and support trainable inner capacities by creating specialised units and positions within the agency responsible for overseeing cross-departmental initiatives. These units should support and coordinate programmes that nurture the cognitive, emotional and relational capacities of citizens and public sector staff in different areas of public life. Particular emphasis should be placed on evidence-based interventions such as mindfulness and compassion training, tailored to foster sustainable transformation across personal, collective and system levels.

2. Education

Policymakers should encourage a more holistic perspective on the purpose of education at all levels; balancing knowledge and skills with the cultivation of foundational inner human capacities, such as mindfulness and compassion, which underpin individual and societal learning, flourishing and sustainability. In particular:

- Policymakers should support teacher education, educational processes, evaluation, ethos and learning environments that foster the development of the whole person, including inner capacities.

- Sustainability education should be a right of every pupil and student, requiring targeted financial government support, dedicated curriculum time and integration across all disciplines and subject areas. Learning about ecological concerns and their important implications for the lives of new generations should be balanced with the development of the inner capacities, like mindfulness and compassion, that are required to cope with the emotional cost and respond appropriately.

- In addition to providing mindfulness and compassion training _in_ education (usually one-off courses deployed to support teacher and student wellbeing), higher education institutions should promote the growing and promising field of mindfulness _as_ education. This approach to teaching uses mindfulness as a means to bring greater awareness, embodiment and critical reflection across the entire learning process.

3. Leadership development

Political, public and private sector institutions should routinely provide training for leaders that supports their understanding and cultivation of inner capacities that will underpin robust action in responding to climate change. In particular:

- Climate leadership training should be provided to decision-makers at all levels, and integrated with mindfulness and compassion-informed practices so that climate change and other sustainability challenges are more comprehensively grasped and acted upon.

- Leaders and their advisors should receive basic education about how the inner and outer dimensions of the climate crisis interrelate, so that they can consider both in their organisations' internal and external sustainability work. For example, understanding of human biases and common psychological defence mechanisms to threatening messages might help communication strategies overcome resistance to challenging climate information and necessary change processes amongst colleagues and stakeholders.

- Politicians in particular should receive basic education about the mechanisms of neurophysiological states like threat response and the prevalence of nervous system dysregulation across society, and their implications for issues like polarisation.

4. Equitable access to training

Governments should ensure that mainstream interventions designed to develop inner capacities for climate action are publicly funded and easy to access in order to avoid exacerbating health and social inequalities. In particular:

- Programmes that support citizens to cultivate inner capacities, like mindfulness and compassion, should be delivered in a variety of contexts and settings (e.g. health care, employment centres).

- Measures should be designed together with target populations and delivered in context-sensitive formats and accessible language so that they can reach a wide cross-section of the population across the life course.

- In order to help offset their own impact on social and health inequality, private training organisations should consider providing free services and support to marginalised and underserved populations by including these costs in their corporate fees, appealing to the Corporate Social Responsibility policies of client companies.

5. Nature connection

In addition to advocating nature-based solutions and ensuring more equitable access to nature, governments and NGOs should provide funding for mindfulness and compassion-informed nature connection opportunities. In particular:

- Local government authorities should provide citizens with accessible mindful nature connection opportunities, such as guided mindfulness walks, in local or nearby natural settings.

- Where feasible, education institutions should arrange for some mindfulness- and compassion-informed learning to take place in natural settings, particularly for sustainability education.

- Wherever possible, leadership development programmes that cultivate inner capacities like mindfulness and compassion to support climate action, as described in Recommendation 3, should take place within natural settings, or include immersive time in wild nature.

- Governments should increase access to nature by establishing or expanding national parks and the right of citizens to access public- and privately-owned green spaces, lakes and rivers for recreation, exercise and conscious connection.

6. Digital technology

In addition to passing regulatory legislation, Governments should support citizens to develop inner capacities, such as mindfulness and compassion, that will help to protect them from the negative impact of products and services of 'big tech'. Many policy recommendations from the Centre for Humane Technology could be informed by and integrated with mindfulness and compassion theory and practice. In particular, the US-based policy institute proposes:

- Publicly funded programs to help people get to know themselves and their weaknesses better than tech does

- Protection for citizens' right to "cognitive liberty"

- Interventions preventing and combating technology/screen addiction

- Draft guidelines from health authorities on fostering healthy child development in the context of digital technology

- Big Tobacco-style publicly funded awareness and literacy campaigns (e.g. 1990's :truth campaign)

7. Health care and health promotion

Public health bodies and health care services should provide support for eco-anxiety, -grief, and -depression particularly for the young, that doesn't unnecessarily pathologise these responses or resort to prescription drugs. Instead, approaches should use mindfulness and compassion-based practices and social support to work through difficult emotions relating to the climate crisis. In addition:

- General practitioners should be trained by sector bodies to recognise the mental health impacts of the climate crisis and provide clear recommendations for non-medical support, in addition to any necessary treatment in the short-term.

- Mental health practitioners within the education sector should be similarly trained to recognise the mental health impacts of the climate crisis and provided with clear referral pathways. This support should be integrated with sustainability education.

- Individual and community wellbeing and flourishing should become a much higher policy priority, reflecting the crucial link between individual and planetary health, and replacing economic growth as the main indicator of societal success.

8. Research

Governmental and research funding bodies should greatly increase funding for research into the linkages between the inner and outer dimensions of sustainability challenges, such as climate change, and the interaction between trainable inner capacities and pro-environmental action across individual, collective and system levels. In particular:

- Research funders should urgently support investigation into the vicious cycle of climate change, threat response and trauma, poor mental health, worldviews of separateness and disengagement. They should further support the development and testing of methods and approaches that may interrupt and reverse this cycle, such as social mindfulness- and compassion-based approaches.

- Researchers should draw upon recent academic reviews, evidence and models for inner and outer transformation as a roadmap for further enquiry. One important line of research and policy in this context is to investigate in more depth how internal qualities and leverage points relate to the United Nations 17 Sustainable Development Goals, and direct resources to their exploration and consideration in organisations, professional groups and society at large. This includes deeper inquiry into how the intersection of mindfulness, compassion and climate change can be best-considered in politics and policymaking.

- Researchers should challenge the assumptions of current scientific approaches to sustainability and climate work: how they conduct research, construct knowledge, and include multiple perspectives and knowledges. Integrative approaches that link inner and outer transformation require change to contemporary knowledge production systems, which are predominantly reliant on a positivist mode of thinking.

9. Innovation

Public sector, private sector and philanthropy organisations should encourage, commission and support innovators to create and adapt mindfulness and compassion interventions to foster climate action. Innovators should be aware of the recommendations in the Mindfulness Initiative's Fieldbook for Mindfulness Innovators. In particular:

- Mindfulness and compassion experts and innovators should critically reflect upon and expand their existing work, incorporating approaches from social and sustainability sciences to better support climate action.

- Innovation should be sensitive to the adaptation requirements for specific settings and cultures. Wherever possible innovators should co-create interventions with target populations.

- Any innovators working with mindfulness-based or -informed interventions should ensure that they have sufficient expertise on their team to safely and effectively create or adapt programmes.

- All mindfulness and compassion interventions should be trauma-informed.

- Innovators should commit to increasing the rigour of testing and research of their interventions over time, collaborating with external researchers after initial phases of development.

The recommendations above build on a robust body of existing work examining the role of mindfulness training in public policy. In 2015, The Mindfulness Initiative and UK All-Party Parliamentary Group on Mindfulness published the first review of mindfulness-based applications in the context of societal needs. The seminal Mindful Nation UK report focused on the policy areas of health, education, criminal justice and the workplace. Many of that report's recommendations for the UK Government are still valid and transferable to other jurisdictions, and further inquiries and briefing papers have since added suggestions for policymakers and practitioners alike. The results of these more sector-specific inquiries can be found on the Mindfulness Initiative website.

References

1   Ioannidis JPA, Boyack KW, Baas J (2020) Updated science-wide author databases of standardized citation indicators. PLOS Biology 18(10): e3000918. https://doi.org/10.1371/journal.pbio.3000918

2   Ives, C. D., Freeth, R., & Fischer, J. (2020). Inside-out sustainability: The neglect of inner worlds. Ambio, 49(1), 208-217.

     Woiwode C., Schäpke N., Bina O., Veciana S., Kunze I., Parodi O., Schweizer-Ries P., Wamsler C. (2021) Inner transformation to sustainability as a deep leverage point: fostering new avenues for change through dialogue and reflection, Sustainability Science, 1-18

     Wamsler, C., Brossmann, J., Hendersson, H., Kristjansdottir, R., McDonald, C. and Scarampi, P. (2018) Mindfulness in sustainability science, practice, and teaching, Sustainability Science, 13(1):143-162

     Göpel, M. (2016). The great mindshift: how a new economic paradigm and sustainability transformations go hand in hand. Springer Nature.

     Horcea-Milcu, A.-I., Abson, D. J., Apetrei, C. I., Duse, I. A., Freeth, R., Riechers, M., Lam, D. P. M., Dorninger, C., & Lang, D. J. (2019). Values in transformational sustainability science: four perspectives for change. In Sustainability Science (Vol. 14, Issue 5, pp. 1425–1437). https://doi.org/10.1007/s11625-019-00656-1

3   Wamsler, C., Osberg, G., Osika, W., Hendersson, H., Mundaca, L. (2021) Linking internal and external transformation for sustainability and climate action: Towards a new research and policy agenda, Global Environmental Change, Volume 71, 102373.

4   IPCC, 2022: Climate Change 2022: Mitigation of Climate Change. Contribution of Working Group III to the Sixth Assessment Report of the Intergovernmental Panel on Climate Change [P.R. Shukla, J. Skea, R. Slade, A. Al Khourdajie, R. van Diemen, D. McCollum, M. Pathak, S. Some, P. Vyas, R. Fradera, M. Belkacemi, A. Hasija, G. Lisboa, S. Luz, J. Malley, (eds.)]. Cambridge University Press, Cambridge, UK and New York, NY, USA. doi: 10.1017/9781009157926

     IPCC, 2022: Climate Change 2022: Impacts, Adaptation, and Vulnerability. Contribution of Working Group II to the Sixth Assessment Report of the Intergovernmental Panel on Climate Change [H.-O. Pörtner, D.C. Roberts, M. Tignor, E.S. Poloczanska, K. Mintenbeck, A. Alegría, M. Craig, S. Langsdorf, S. Löschke, V. Möller, A. Okem, B. Rama (eds.)]. Cambridge University Press. In Press.

     Wamsler, C., Osberg, G., Osika, W., Hendersson, H., Mundaca, L. (2021) Linking internal and external transformation for sustainability and climate action: Towards a new research and policy agenda, Global Environmental Change, Volume 71, 102373.

5   Wamsler, C., Bristow, J. (2022) At the intersection of mind and climate: Integrating inner dimensions of climate change into policymaking, forthcoming.

6   Fukushima, H., Terasawa, Y., & Umeda, S. (2011). Association between interoception and empathy: Evidence from heartbeat-evoked brain potential. International Journal of Psychophysiology, 79(2), 259–265. https://doi.org/10.1016/j.ijpsycho.2010.10.015

7   Wamsler, C., Brossmann, J., Hendersson, H., Kristjansdottir, R., McDonald, C. and Scarampi, P. (2018) Mindfulness in sustainability science, practice, and teaching, Sustainability Science, 13(1):143-162. Online.

     Wamsler, C., Osberg, G., Osika, W., Herndersson, H., & Mundaca, L. (2021). Linking internal and external transformation for sustainability and climate action: Towards a new research and policy agenda. Global Environmental Change, 71, 102373.

8   Strauss, C., Lever Taylor, B., Gu, J., Kuyken, W., Baer, R., Jones, F., & Cavanagh, K. (2016). What is compassion and how can we measure it? A review of definitions and measures. Clinical Psychology Review, 47, 15–27.

9   Baminiwatta, A., & Solangaarachchi, I. (2021). Trends and developments in mindfulness research over 55 years: A bibliometric analysis of publications indexed in Web of Science. Mindfulness, 12(9), 2099-2116.

     Wamsler, C., Osberg, G., Osika, W., Hendersson, H., Mundaca, L. (2021) Linking internal and external transformation for sustainability and climate action: Towards a new research and policy agenda, Global Environmental Change, Volume 71.

10   Wamsler, C., Bristow, J. (2022) At the intersection of mind and climate: Integrating inner dimensions of climate change into policymaking, forthcoming.

11   O'Brien, K., & Hochachka, G. (2010). Integral adaptation to climate change. Journal of Integral Theory and Practice, 5(1), 89-102.;

Hochachka, G. (2021). Integrating the four faces of climate change adaptation: Towards transformative change in Guatemalan coffee communities. World Development, 140, 105361.

12   Tang, Y., Hölzel, B., & Posner, M. (2015). The neuroscience of mindfulness meditation. Nature Reviews Neuroscience, 16(4), 213-225.

Schneider, J., Malinowski, P., Watson, P., & Lattimore, P. (2019). The role of mindfulness in physical activity: a systematic review. Obesity Reviews, 20(3), 448-463.

13   Thiermann, U. B., Sheate, W. R., & Vercammen, A. (2020). Practice matters: Pro-environmental motivations and diet-related impact vary with meditation experience. Frontiers in psychology, 3577.

14   Geiger, S. M., Grossman, P., & Schrader, U. (2018). Mindfulness and sustainability: Correlation or causation? Current Opinion in Psychology, 28, 23–27. https://doi.org/10.1016/j.copsyc.2018.09.010

15   Wamsler, C., Osberg, G., Osika, W., Hendersson, H., Mundaca, L. (2021) Linking internal and external transformation for sustainability and climate action: Towards a new research and policy agenda, Global Environmental Change, Volume 71.

16   IPCC, 2022: Climate Change 2022: Mitigation of Climate Change. Contribution of Working Group III to the Sixth Assessment Report of the Intergovernmental Panel on Climate Change [P.R. Shukla, J. Skea, R. Slade, A. Al Khourdajie, R. van Diemen, D. McCollum, M. Pathak, S. Some, P. Vyas, R. Fradera, M. Belkacemi, A. Hasija, G. Lisboa, S. Luz, J. Malley, (eds.)]. Cambridge University Press, Cambridge, UK and New York, NY, USA. doi: 10.1017/9781009157926

17   Wamsler, C., Schäpke, N., Fraude, C., Stasiak, D., Bruhn, T., Lawrence, M., ... & Mundaca, L. (2020). Enabling new mindsets and transformative skills for negotiating and activating climate action: Lessons from UNFCCC conferences of the parties. Environmental science & policy, 112, 227-235.

18   Wamsler, C., Osberg, G., Osika, W., Herndersson, H., & Mundaca, L. (2021). Linking internal and external transformation for sustainability and climate action: Towards a new research and policy agenda. Global Environmental Change, 71, 102373.

19   Wamsler, C., Osberg, G., Osika, W., Hendersson, H., Mundaca, L. (2021) Linking internal and external transformation for sustainability and climate action: Towards a new research and policy agenda, Global Environmental Change, Volume 71, 102373.

20   Newen, A., De Bruin, L., & Gallagher, S. (Eds.). (2018). The Oxford handbook of 4E cognition. Oxford University Press.

21   Archibald, J. A. (2008). *Indigenous storywork: Educating the heart, mind, body, and spirit*. UBC press.

Lin, C. T. (2013). Rethinking mind-body dualism: a Buddhist take on the mind-body problem. *Contemporary Buddhism, 14(2)*, 239-264.

Siegel, D. (2022). IntraConnected: MWe (Me + We) As the Integration of Self, Identity, and Belonging. W. W. Norton & Company. Forthcoming.

22   Dehaene, S. (2020). How We Learn: The New Science of Education and the Brain, Chapter 7: Attention. Penguin

23   Olson, R. L., & Rejeski, D. (2018). Slow threats and environmental policy. *Envtl. L. Rep. News & Analysis, 48*, 10116.

24   Hadot, P. (1995). Philosophy as a Way of Life. Blackwell. Oxford, UK.

25   Williams, J. (2018). Stand out of our light: Freedom and resistance in the attention economy. Cambridge University Press. Cambridge, UK.

26   Wu, T. (2016). The Attention Merchants: How Our Time and Attention Are Gathered and Sold. Atlantic Analysis Corp. Norfolk, VA, United States

27   Misra, S., Cheng, L., Genevie, J., Et al. (2014). The iPhone Effect: The Quality of In-Person Social Interactions in the Presence of Mobile Devices. Research Article. https://doi.org/10.1177/0013916514539755

28   Turkle, S. (2011). Alone together: Why we expect more from technology and less from ourselves: New York: Basic Books

29   Harmon, J., & Duffy, L. (2021). Alienation from leisure: Smartphones and the loss of presence. Leisure/Loisir, 1-21.

30   Richardson, M., Hussain, Z., & Griffiths, M. D. (2018). Problematic smartphone use, nature connectedness, and anxiety. Journal of Behavioral Addictions, 7(1), 109-116.

31   Bamberg, S., Rees, J. H., & Schulte, M. (2018). Environmental protection through societal change: What psychology knows about collective climate action—and what it needs to find out. In Psychology and climate change (pp. 185-213). Academic Press.

32   Williams, J.M.G., (2009). Mindfulness, Depression and Modes of Mind. Cogn Ther Res 32, 721. https://doi.org/10.1007/s10608-008-9204-z

33   Greenberg, J., Romero, V., Elkin-Frankston, S., Bezdek, M., Schumacher, E., & Lazar, S. (2018). Reduced interference in working memory following mindfulness training is associated with increases in hippocampal volume. Brain Imaging and Behavior, 13(2), 366-376.

34   Cásedas, L., Pirruccio, V., Vadillo, M., & Lupiáñez, J. (2020). Does Mindfulness Meditation Training Enhance Executive Control? A Systematic Review and Meta-Analysis of Randomized Controlled Trials in Adults. Mindfulness, 11(2), 411-424.

35   Goldberg, S. B., Riordan, K. M., Sun, S., & Davidson, R. J. (2022). The Empirical Status of Mindfulness-Based Interventions: A Systematic Review of 44 Meta-Analyses of Randomized Controlled Trials. Perspectives on Psychological Science: A Journal of the Association for Psychological Science, 17(1), 108–130.

        Goldberg, S. B., Tucker, R. P., Greene, P. A., Davidson, R. J., Kearney, D. J., & Simpson, T. L. (2019). Mindfulness-based cognitive therapy for the treatment of current depressive symptoms: A meta-analysis. Cognitive Behaviour Therapy. https://www.ncbi.nlm.nih.gov/pubmed/30732534

        Khoo, E.-L. L., Small, R., Cheng, W., Hatchard, T., Glynn, B., Rice, D. B., Skidmore, B., Kenny, S., Hutton, B., & Poulin, P. A. (2019). Comparative evaluation of group-based mindfulness-based stress reduction and cognitive behavioural therapy for the treatment and management of chronic pain: A systematic review and network meta-analysis. Evid Based Ment Health, 22(1), 26–35. https://doi.org/10.1136/ebmental-2018-300062

36   Goldberg, S. B., Riordan, K. M., Sun, S., & Davidson, R. J. (2022). The Empirical Status of Mindfulness-Based Interventions: A Systematic Review of 44 Meta-Analyses of Randomized Controlled Trials. Perspectives on Psychological Science: A Journal of the Association for Psychological Science, 17(1), 108–130.

37   Querstret, D., Morison, L., Dickinson, S., Cropley, M., & John, M. (2020). Mindfulness-Based Stress Reduction and Mindfulness-Based Cognitive Therapy for Psychological Health and Well-Being in Nonclinical Samples: A Systematic Review and Meta-Analysis. International Journal of Stress Management, 27(4), 394-411.

38   Victorson, D., Sauer, C., Wolters, L., Maletich, C., Lukoff, K., & Sufrin, N. (2020). Meta-analysis of Technology-Enabled Mindfulness-Based Programs for Negative Affect and Mindful Awareness. Mindfulness, 11(8), 1884-1899.

39   Vonderlin, R., Biermann, M., Bohus, M., & Lyssenko, L. (2020). Mindfulness-Based Programs in the Workplace: a Meta-Analysis of Randomized Controlled Trials. Mindfulness, 11(7), 1579-1598.

40   Gill, L. N., Renault, R., Campbell, E., Rainville, P., & Khoury, B. (2020). Mindfulness induction and cognition: A systematic review and meta-analysis. Consciousness and Cognition, 84, 102991.

        Whitfield, T., Barnhofer, T., Acabchuk, R., Cohen, A., Lee, M., Schlosser, M., Arenaza-Urquijo, E. M., Böttcher, A., Britton, W., Coll-Padros, N., Collette, F., Chételat, G., Dautricourt, S., Demnitz-King, H., Dumais, T., Klimecki, O., Meiberth, D., Moulinet, I., Müller, T., ... Marchant, N. L. (2021). The Effect of Mindfulness-based Programs on Cognitive Function in Adults: A Systematic Review and Meta-analysis. Neuropsychology Review. https://doi.org/10.1007/s11065-021-09519-y

41   Donald, J., Sahdra, B., Van Zanden, B., Duineveld, J., Atkins, P., Marshall, S., & Ciarrochi, J. (2019). Does your mindfulness benefit others? A systematic review and meta analysis of the link between mindfulness and prosocial behaviour. British Journal of Psychology, 110(1), 101-125.

42   Berry, D., Hoerr, J., Cesko, S., Alayoubi, A., Carpio, K., Zirzow, H., Walters, W., Scram, G., Rodriguez, K., & Beaver, V. (2020). Does Mindfulness Training Without Explicit Ethics-Based Instruction Promote Prosocial Behaviors? A Meta-Analysis. Personality and Social Psychology Bulletin, 46(8), 1247-1269.

43   Rachael A. Heckenberg, Pennie Eddy, Stephen Kent, Bradley J. Wright, Do workplace-based mindfulness meditation programs improve physiological indices of stress? A systematic review and meta-analysis, Journal of Psychosomatic Research, https://doi.org/10.1016/j.jpsychores.2018.09.010.

44   Scott-Sheldon, L.J., Gathright, E.C., Donahue, M.L., Balletto, .B., Feulner, M.M., DeCosta, .J., Cruess, D.G., Wing, R.R., Carey, M.P., & Salmoirago-Blotcher, .E. (2020). Mindfulness-Based Interventions for Adults with Cardiovascular Disease: A Systematic Review and Meta-Analysis. Annals of Behavioral Medicine, 54(1),

45   Meditation and telomere length: a meta-analysis Nicola S. Schutte,John M. Malouff &Shian-Ling Keng Pages 901-915 | Received 20 Mar 2019, Accepted 17 Dec 2019, Published online: 05 Jan 2020 Download citation https://doi.org/10.1080/08870446.2019.1707827

46   Goldberg, S. B., Tucker, R. P., Greene, P. A., Simpson, T. L., Kearney, D. J., & Davidson, R. J. (2017). Is mindfulness research methodology improving over time? A systematic review. PloS One, 12(10), e0187298.

47   Congleton, C.,Hölzel, B., K., and Lazar, S., W. (2015, January 08). Mindfulness Can Literally Change Your Brain. Harvard Business Review. https://hbr.org/2015/01/mindfulness-can-literally-change-your-brain

48   Zeidan, F., Martucci, K. T., Kraft, R. A., Gordon, N. S., McHaffie, J. G., & Coghill, R. C. (2011). Brain mechanisms supporting the modulation of pain by mindfulness meditation. *The Journal of Neuroscience: The Official Journal of the Society for Neuroscience*, 31(14), 5540–5548.

49   Moore, A. W., Gruber, T., Derose, J., & Malinowski, P. (2012). Regular, brief mindfulness meditation practice improves electrophysiological markers of attentional control. *Frontiers in human neuroscience, 6*, 18.

50   Lupyan, G. (2015). Cognitive Penetrability of Perception in the Age of Prediction: Predictive Systems are Penetrable Systems. Review of Philosophy and Psychology, 6(4), 547-569.;

51   Kirchhoff, M. D., & Kiverstein, J. (2019). Extended consciousness and predictive processing: A third-wave view. Routledge.

52   Brugger, P., & Brugger, S. (1993). The Easter bunny in October: Is it disguised as a duck?. *Perceptual and motor skills*, 76(2), 577-578.

53   Nickerson, R. S. (1998). Confirmation bias: A ubiquitous phenomenon in many guises. Review of general psychology, 2(2), 175-220.

54   Langer, E. J. (2000). Mindful learning. Current directions in psychological science, 9(6), 220-223.

55   Wamsler C. (2020) Education for sustainability: Fostering a more conscious society and transformation towards sustainability, International Journal of Sustainability in Higher Education 21(1):112-130. Online.

56   McCown, D., Riebel, D., Micozzi, M. (2010) Teaching Mindfulness.

57   Crane, R.S., Brewer, J., Feldman, C., Kabat-Zinn, J., Santorelli, S., Williams, J.M.G., Kuyken, W., (2017). What defines mindfulness-based programs? The warp and the weft. DOI: https://doi.org/10.1017/S0033291716003317

58   Wamsler, C., Osberg, G., Osika, W., Hendersson, H., Mundaca, L. (2021) Linking internal and external transformation for sustainability and climate action: Towards a new research and policy agenda, Global Environmental Change, Volume 71. Online.

    Wamsler C. (2020) Education for sustainability: Fostering a more conscious society and transformation towards sustainability, International Journal of Sustainability in Higher Education 21(1):112-130. Online.

    Wamsler, C., Hertog, I., Di Paola, L. (2022) Education for sustainability: Sourcing inner qualities and capacities for transformation. In: Revolutionizing sustainability education: Stories and tools of mindset transformation, Ivanova E., Rimanoczy (Eds.), Routledge. See here.

Frank, P., Fischer, D. and Wamsler, C. (2019) Mindfulness, Education, and the Sustainable Development Goals. In: Encyclopedia of the UN Sustainable Development Goals, Quality Education, Leal Filho, W., Azul, L., Brandli, P., Özuyar, G. and Wall, T. (Eds), Springer. Online.

Wamsler, C. (2019) Contemplative Sustainable Futures: The role of individual inner dimensions and transformation in sustainability research and education. In: Sustainability and the Humanities, Leal Filho, W. and McCrea, A. C. (Eds), Springer

59   Opotow, S., & Weiss, L. (2000). Denial and the process of moral exclusion in environmental conflict. Journal of Social Issues, 56(3), 475-490.

Kahn, S., & Zeidler, D. (2019). A Conceptual Analysis of Perspective Taking in Support of Socioscientific Reasoning. Science & Education, 28(7), 605-638.

Böhm, M., Barkmann, J., Eggert, S., Carstensen, C., & Bögeholz, S. (2020). Quantitative Modelling and Perspective Taking: Two Competencies of Decision Making for Sustainable Development. Sustainability, 12(17),

60   Shahen, M., Kotani, K., & Saijo, T. (2020). Does perspective-taking promotes intergenerational sustainability. Research Institute for Future Design; Working paper SDES-2020-12; Kochi University of Technology: Kochi, Japan.

Rothermich, K., Johnson, E. K., Griffith, R. M., & Beingolea, M. M. (2021). The influence of personality traits on attitudes towards climate change—An exploratory study. Personality and Individual Differences, 168, 110304.

61   Moore, A., Peter Malinowski, P., (2009) Meditation, mindfulness and cognitive flexibility. Consciousness and Cognition 18 (2009) 176–186. doi:10.1016/j.concog.2008.12.008

62   Langer, E., & Moldoveanu, M. (2000). The Construct of Mindfulness. Journal of Social Issues, 56(1).

Block Lerner, J., Adair, C., Plumb, J., Rhatigan, D., & Orsillo, S. (2007). The case for mindfulness based approaches in the cultivation of empathy: Does nonjudgmental, present moment awareness increase capacity for perspective taking and empathic concern?. Journal of Marital and Family Therapy, 33(4).

Karremans, J. C., van Schie, H. T., van Dongen, I., Kappen, G., Mori, G., van As, S., ... & van der Wal, R. C. (2020). Is mindfulness associated with interpersonal forgiveness?. Emotion, 20(2), 296.

63   Bihari, J., & Mullan, E. (2012). Relating Mindfully: A Qualitative Exploration of Changes in Relationships Through Mindfulness-Based Cognitive Therapy. Mindfulness, 5(1), 46-59.

Allen, M., Bromley, A., Kuyken, W., and Sonnenberg, S.J., (2009). Participants' Experiences of Mindfulness-Based Cognitive Therapy: "It Changed Me in Just about Every Way Possible". Behavioural and Cognitive Psychotherapy, 2009, 37, 413–430 doi:10.1017/S135246580999004X

Dunoon, D., Langer, E., (2011). "Mindfulness and Leadership: Opening up to Possibilities." Integral Leadership Review 11 (5) (October):1-15

64   Carson, S.H., Langer, E.J. Mindfulness and self-acceptance. J Rat-Emo Cognitive-Behav Ther 24, 29–43 (2006). https://doi.org/10.1007/s10942-006-0022-

65   H lzel, B., Lazar, S., Gard, T., Schuman-Olivier, Z., Vago, D., & Ott, U. (2011). How Does Mindfulness Meditation Work? Proposing Mechanisms of Action From a Conceptual and Neural Perspective. Perspectives on Psychological Science, 6(6), 537-559.

66   Bristow, J. (2019). Mindfulness in politics and public policy. Current Opinion in Psychology, 28, 87-91.

67   Donald, J., Sahdra, B., Van Zanden, B., Duineveld, J., Atkins, P., Marshall, S., & Ciarrochi, J. (2019). Does your mindfulness benefit others? A systematic review and meta analysis of the link between mindfulness and prosocial behaviour. British Journal of Psychology, 110(1), 101-125.

68   Kabat-Zinn, J. (2011). Some reflections on the origins of MBSR, skillful means, and the trouble with maps. In Contemporary Buddhism (Vol. 12, Issue 1, pp. 281–306). https://doi.org/10.1080/14639947.2011.564844

Segal, Z. V., Williams, J. M. G., & Teasdale, J. D. (2001). Mindfulness-Based Cognitive Therapy for Depression, First Edition: A New Approach to Preventing Relapse. Guilford Publications.

69   Poulin, M. J., Ministero, L. M., Gabriel, S., Morrison, C. D., & Naidu, E. (2021). Minding Your Own Business? Mindfulness Decreases Prosocial Behavior for People With Independent Self-Construals. Psychological Science, 32(11), 1699–1708.

70   Poulin, M. J., Ministero, L. M., Gabriel, S., Morrison, C. D., & Naidu, E. (2021). Minding Your Own Business? Mindfulness Decreases Prosocial Behavior for People With Independent Self-Construals. Psychological Science, 32(11), 1699–1708.

71   Shapiro, D.H. (1992). A preliminary study of long term meditators: Goals, effects, religious orientation, cognitions. Journal of Transpersonal Psychology, 24(1), 23–39.

72   Kabat-Zinn, J. (2005). Coming to our senses: Healing ourselves and the world through mindfulness. New York: Hyperion.

73   TED (Producer). (2006). Do schools kill creativity? Sir Ken Robinson [Video file]. Retrieved from https://www.ted.com/talks/sir_ken_robinson_do_schools_kill_creativity

74   Paul, A., M. (2022). The Extended Mind. HMH Books; McGilchrist, I. (2015) The Master and His Emissary. Yale University Press

75   Lee, B.Y. (2016). 'Save The Planet' Really Should Be 'Save Humans'. Retrieved December 05, 2021, from Forbes website: https://www.forbes.com/sites/brucelee/2016/11/13/why-you-shouldnt-tell-donald-trump-to-save-the-planet/

76   Newen, A., De Bruin, L., & Gallagher, S. (Eds.). (2018). The Oxford handbook of 4E cognition. Oxford University Press.

77   Schultchen, D., Bayer, J., Kühnel, J., Melchers, K., & Pollatos, O. (2019). Interoceptive accuracy is related to long-term stress via self regulation. Psychophysiology, 56(10), n/a-n/a.

        Fazekas, C., Avian, A., Noehrer, R., Matzer, F., Vajda, C., Hannich, H., & Neubauer, A. (2020). Interoceptive awareness and self-regulation contribute to psychosomatic competence as measured by a new inventory. Wiener Klinische Wochenschrift, 1-12.
        Hanley, A. W., Mehling, W. E., & Garland, E. L. (2017). Holding the body in mind: Interoceptive awareness, dispositional mindfulness and psychological well-being. Journal of psychosomatic research, 99, 13-20.

        Hübner AM, Trempler I, Gietmann C, Schubotz RI (2021) Interoceptive sensibility predicts the ability to infer others' emotional states. PLoS ONE 16(10): e0258089. https://doi.org/10.1371/journal.pone.0258089

        Dobrushina, O. R., Dobrynina, L. A., Arina, G. A., Kremneva, E. I., Suslina, A. D., Gubanova, M. V., ... & Krotenkova, M. V. (2020). Interaction of interoceptive perception and emotional intelligence: a functional neuroimaging study. Neuroscience and Behavioral Physiology, 50(8), 1043-1050.
        Werner, N., Schweitzer, N., Meindl, T., Duschek, S., Kambeitz, J., & Schandry, R. (2013). Interoceptive awareness moderates neural activity during decision-making. Biological Psychology, 94(3), 498-506.

        Grynberg, D., & Pollatos, O. (2015). Perceiving one's body shapes empathy. Physiology & behavior, 140, 54-60.

        Heydrich, L., Walker, F., Blättler, L., Herbelin, B., Blanke, O., & Aspell, J. E. (2021). Interoception and empathy impact perspective taking. Frontiers in psychology, 11, 4016.

78   Fukushima, H., Terasawa, Y., & Umeda, S. (2011). Association between interoception and empathy: Evidence from heartbeat-evoked brain potential. International Journal of Psychophysiology, 79(2), 259–265. https://doi.org/10.1016/j.ijpsycho.2010.10.015

79   Khoury, B., Knäuper, B., Pagnini, F., Trent, N., Chiesa, A., & Carrière, K. (2017). Embodied Mindfulness. Mindfulness, 8(5), 1160-1171.

80   Crane, R.S., Brewer, J., Feldman, C., Kabat-Zinn, J., Santorelli, S., Williams, J.M.G., Kuyken, W., (2017). What defines mindfulness-based programs? The warp and the weft. DOI: https://doi.org/10.1017/S0033291716003317

81   Treves, I., Tello, L., Davidson, R., & Goldberg, S. (2019). The relationship between mindfulness and objective measures of body awareness: A meta-analysis. Scientific Reports, 9(1), 1-12.

82   Hölzel, B., Lazar, S., Gard, T., Schuman-Olivier, Z., Vago, D., & Ott, U. (2011). How Does Mindfulness Meditation Work? Proposing Mechanisms of Action From a Conceptual and Neural Perspective. Perspectives on Psychological Science, 6(6), 537-559.
Fox, K. C. et al. Is meditation associated with altered Brain structure? A systematic review and meta-analysis of morphometric neuroimaging in meditation practitioners. Neurosci. Biobehav. Rev. 43, 48-73 (2014).

83   Porges, S. W., & Carter, C. S. (2017). Polyvagal theory and the social engagement system. Complementary and Integrative Treatments in Psychiatric Practice. Washington DC, American Psychiatric Association Publishing, 221-241.

84   Donahue, J. J. (2020). Fight-flight-freeze system. Encyclopedia of personality and individual differences, 1590-1595.

85   Fight, Flight, Freeze: What This Response Means. (n.d.). Retrieved Feb 20, 2022, from Healthline website: https://www.healthline.com/health/mental-health/fight-flight-freeze#in-the-body

86   Weltman, G., Smith, J. E., & Egstrom, G. H. (1971). Perceptual narrowing during simulated pressure-chamber exposure. Human Factors, 13(2), 99-107.

        Pessink, M. A. (1998). The Effects of the Sympathetic Nervous System on Officers Involved in Critical Incidents and the Application of this Information to Post Incident Investigations.

87   Siegel, D. (2019). The mind in psychotherapy: An interpersonal neurobiology framework for understanding and cultivating mental health. Psychology and Psychotherapy: Theory, Research and Practice, 92(2), 224-237.

88   Andrews, N., & Hoggett, P. (2019). Facing up to ecological crisis: A psychosocial perspective from climate psychology. Facing up to Climate Reality: Honesty, Disaster and Hope; Foster, J. , Ed, 155–171.

89   A LARGER US. (2018). The Collective Psychology Project. A Larger Us website: https://larger.us/ideas/?report

90   Slutsky, J., Rahl, H., Lindsay, E. K., & Creswell, J. D. (2017). Mindfulness, emotion regulation, and social threat. In Mindfulness in social psychology (pp. 79-93). Routledge.

91   Chin, M. S., & Kales, S. N. (2019). Understanding mind–body disciplines: A pilot study of paced breathing and dynamic muscle contraction on autonomic nervous system reactivity. Stress and Health, 35(4), 542-548.

92   Dutcher, J. M., Boyle, C. C., Eisenberger, N. I., Cole, S. W., & Bower, J. E. (2021). Neural responses to threat and reward and changes in inflammation following a mindfulness intervention. Psychoneuroendocrinology, 125, 105114.

93   Kozlowska, K., Walker, P., McLean, L., & Carrive, P. (2015). Fear and the defense cascade: clinical implications and management. Harvard review of psychiatry.

94   Lanius, R. Rethinking Trauma: How Neuroscience Can Give Us a Clearer Picture of Trauma Treatment. National Institute for the Clinical Application of Behavioural Medicine. Retrieved Feb 20, 2022, from NICABM Psychology Today website: https://s3.amazonaws.com/nicabm-stealthseminar/Rethinking-trauma-new/Ruth/NICABM-RuthLanius-Transcript.pdf via https://www.nicabm.com/program/trauma-lanius/

95   Fisher, J. (2017). Healing the fragmented selves of trauma survivors: Overcoming internal self-alienation. Routledge. Forner, C. (2017). Dissociation, mindfulness and creative meditations. Trauma-informed practices to facilitate growth. New York: Routledge

96   Epstein, M. (2014). The trauma of everyday life. Penguin.

97   Lehrner, A., & Yehuda, R. (2018). Trauma Across Generations and Paths to Adaptation and Resilience. Psychological Trauma: Theory, Research, Practice, and Policy, 10(1), 22-29.

        Audergon, A. (2004). Collective trauma: the nightmare of history. Psychotherapy and Politics International, 2(1), 16-31.

        Flanagan, N., Travers, A., Vallières, F., Hansen, M., Halpin, R., Sheaf, G., ... & Johnsen, A. T. (2020). Crossing borders: A systematic review identifying potential mechanisms of intergenerational trauma transmission in asylum-seeking and refugee families. European Journal of Psychotraumatology, 11(1), 1790283.

98   Bednarek, S. (2021). Climate change, fragmentation and collective trauma. Bridging the divided stories we live by. Journal of Social Work Practice, 35(1), 5-17.

99   Jackson, L., Jackson, Z., & Jackson, F. (2018). Intergenerational resilience in response to the stress and trauma of enslavement and chronic exposure to institutionalized racism. Journal of Clinical Epigenetics, 4(3), 2472-1158.

        Macia, K., Moschetto, J., Wickham, R., Brown, L., & Waelde, L. (2020). Cumulative Trauma Exposure and Chronic Homelessness Among Veterans: The Roles of Responses to Intrusions and Emotion Regulation. Journal of Traumatic Stress, 33(6), 1017-1028.

        Hübl, T., & Avritt, J. J. (2020). Healing collective trauma: A process for integrating our intergenerational and cultural wounds. Sounds True.

100   Bloom, S. (2004). Neither liberty nor safety: the impact of fear on individuals, institutions, and societies, part I. Psychotherapy and Politics International, 2(2), 78-98.

101   Banschick, M. Somatic Experiencing: How trauma can be overcome. (26 March, 2015). Retrieved Feb 20, 2022, from Psychology Today website: https://www.psychologytoday.com/gb/blog/the-intelligent-divorce/201503/somatic-experiencing

102   Adair, K., Fredrickson, B., Castro-Schilo, L., Kim, S., & Sidberry, S. (2017). Present with You: Does Cultivated Mindfulness Predict Greater Social Connection Through Gains in Decentering and Reductions in Negative Emotions?. Mindfulness, 9(3), 737-749.

        Donald, J., Bradshaw, E., Ryan, R., Basarkod, G., Ciarrochi, J., Duineveld, J., Guo, J., & Sahdra, B. (2020). Mindfulness and Its Association With Varied Types of Motivation: A Systematic Review and Meta-Analysis Using Self-Determination Theory. Personality and Social Psychology Bulletin, 46(7), 1121-1138.

        Price, C. J., & Hooven, C. (2018). Interoceptive awareness skills for emotion regulation: Theory and approach of mindful awareness in body-oriented therapy (MABT). Frontiers in psychology, 9, 798.

103   Winders, S. J., Murphy, O., Looney, K., & O'Reilly, G. (2020). Self compassion, trauma, and posttraumatic stress disorder: A systematic review. Clinical Psychology & Psychotherapy, 27(3), 300-329.

104   Shiyko, M., Hallinan, S., & Naito, T. (2017). Effects of Mindfulness Training on Posttraumatic Growth: a Systematic Review and Meta-Analysis. Mindfulness, 8(4), 848-858.

        Chan, B. S. M., Deng, J., Li, Y., Li, T., Shen, Y., Wang, Y., & Yi, L. (2020). The role of self-compassion in the relationship between post-traumatic growth and psychological distress in caregivers of children with autism. Journal of Child and Family Studies, 29(6), 1692-1700.

        Doppelt, B. (2017). Transformational resilience: how building human resilience to climate disruption can safeguard society and increase wellbeing. Routledge.

105   Bohus, M., Kleindienst, N., Hahn, C., Müller-Engelmann, M., Ludäscher, P., Steil, R., Fydrich, T., Kuehner, C., Resick, P., Stiglmayr, C., Schmahl, C., & Priebe, K. (2020). Dialectical Behavior Therapy for Posttraumatic Stress Disorder (DBT-PTSD) Compared With Cognitive Processing Therapy (CPT) in Complex Presentations of PTSD in Women Survivors of Childhood Abuse. JAMA Psychiatry, 77(12), 1235-1245.

106   Treleaven, D. A. (2018). Trauma-sensitive mindfulness: Practices for safe and transformative healing. WW Norton & Company.

107   Treleaven, D. A. (2018). Trauma-sensitive mindfulness: Practices for safe and transformative healing. WW Norton & Company.

108   Winders, S.-J., Murphy, O., Looney, K., & O'Reilly, G. (2020). Self-compassion, trauma, and posttraumatic stress disorder: A systematic review. Clinical Psychology & Psychotherapy, 27(3), 300–329.

109   Kuyken, W., Warren, F., Taylor, R., Whalley, B., Crane, C., Bondolfi, G., Segal, Z. (2016). Efficacy of mindfulness-based cognitive therapy in prevention of depressive relapse: An individual patient data meta-analysis from randomized trials. JAMA Psychiatry, 73, 565-574.

110   Baer, R., Crane, C., Miller, E., & Kuyken, W. (2019). Doing no harm in mindfulness-based programs: conceptual issues and empirical findings. Clinical psychology review, 71, 101-114.

111   Harari, Y. N. (2014). Sapiens: a brief history of humankind. London: Vintage Books. ISBN: 9781846558245.

112   Bodenhorn, B. (2020). On Being Selfish—Or Not. Selfishness and Selflessness: New Approaches to Understanding Morality, 10, 199.

113   Colquhoun, L., Workman, L., Fowler, J. (2020). The Problem of Altruism and Future Directions. In Barkow, J.H., Workman,L., Reader, W. (Ed.), The Cambridge Handbook of Evolutionary Perspectives on Human Behavior. Cambridge University Press. Singer, P. (1981). Expanding Circle. 237 Pinker, S., (2011). The Better Angels of Our Nature: Why Violence Has Declined. Penguin. London, UK

114   Colquhoun, L., Workman, L., Fowler, J. (2020). The Problem of Altruism and Future Directions. In Barkow, J.H., Workman,L., Reader, W. (Ed.), The Cambridge Handbook of Evolutionary Perspectives on Human Behavior. Cambridge University Press.

115   Mayer, J., Salovey, P., & Caruso, D. (2008). Emotional Intelligence. American Psychologist, 63(6), 503-517.

        Goleman, D. (2020). Emotional intelligence. Bloomsbury Publishing.

        Drigas, A., & Papoutsi, C. (2018). A New Layered Model on Emotional Intelligence. Behavioral Sciences, 8(5), 45

116   Wamsler C., Restoy, F. (2020) Emotional Intelligence and the Sustainable Development Goals: Supporting peaceful, just and inclusive societies. In: Encyclopedia of the UN Sustainable Development Goals, Peace, Justice and Strong Institutions, Leal Filho, W., Azul, L., Brandli, P., Özuyar, G. and Wall, T. (Eds.). Springer. Online.

117   Mayer, J. D., Roberts, R. D., & Barsade, S. G. (2008). Human abilities: Emotional intelligence. Annu. Rev. Psychol., 59, 507-536.

118   MacCann, C., Jiang, Y., Brown, L. E., Double, K. S., Bucich, M., & Minbashian, A. (2020). Emotional intelligence predicts academic performance: A meta-analysis. Psychological Bulletin, 146(2), 150.

        Joseph DL, Jin J, Newman DA, O'Boyle EH (2015). "Why does self-reported emotional intelligence predict job performance? A meta-analytic investigation of mixed EI". The Journal of Applied Psychology. 100 (2): 298–342. doi:10.1037/a0037681. PMID 25243996.

119   Wamsler C. (2020) Education for sustainability: Fostering a more conscious society and transformation towards sustainability, International Journal of Sustainability in Higher Education 21(1):112-130.

        Wamsler C., Restoy, F. (2020) Emotional Intelligence and the Sustainable Development Goals: Supporting peaceful, just and inclusive societies. In: Encyclopedia of the UN Sustainable Development Goals, Peace, Justice and Strong Institutions, Leal Filho, W., Azul, L., Brandli, P., Özuyar, G. and Wall, T. (Eds.). Springer.

120   Jiménez-Picón, N., Romero-Martín, M., Ponce-Blandón, J., Ramirez-Baena, L., Palomo-Lara, J., & Gómez-Salgado, J. (2021). The Relationship between Mindfulness and Emotional Intelligence as a Protective Factor for Healthcare Professionals: Systematic Review. International Journal of Environmental Research and Public Health, 18(10),

        Nadler, R., Carswell, J., & Minda, J. (2020). Online Mindfulness Training Increases Well-Being, Trait Emotional Intelligence, and Workplace Competency Ratings: A Randomized Waitlist-Controlled Trial. Frontiers in Psychology, 11

        Teper,R.; Inzlicht, M. (2013). Meditation, mindfulness and executive control: the importance of emotional acceptance and brain-based performance monitoring. Social Cognitive and Affective Neuroscience, 8:1, 85–92, https://doi.org/10.1093/scan/nss045

        Wheeler, M., Arnkoff, D., & Glass, C. (2017). The Neuroscience of Mindfulness: How Mindfulness Alters the Brain and Facilitates Emotion Regulation. Mindfulness, 8(6), 1471-1487.

        Luberto, C., Shinday, N., Song, R., Philpotts, L., Park, E., Fricchione, G., & Yeh, G. (2017). A Systematic Review and Meta-analysis of the Effects of Meditation on Empathy, Compassion, and Prosocial Behaviors. Mindfulness, 9(3), 708-724.

        Jones, S., Bodie, G., & Hughes, S. (2019). The Impact of Mindfulness on Empathy, Active Listening, and Perceived Provisions of Emotional Support. Communication Research, 46(6), 838-865.
        Cheang, R., Gillions, A., & Sparkes, E. (2019). Do Mindfulness-Based Interventions Increase Empathy and Compassion in Children and Adolescents: A Systematic Review. Journal of Child and Family Studies, 28(7), 1765-1779.

121 Adam A. Kaya, A.A., Skarlicki, D.P., (2017). Cultivating a conflict-positive workplace: How mindfulness facilitates constructive conflict management. Organizational Behavior and Human Decision Processes journal homepage: www.elsevier.com/locate/obhdp

122 Karremans, J., Schellekens, M., & Kappen, G. (2017). Bridging the Sciences of Mindfulness and Romantic Relationships. Personality and Social Psychology Review, 21(1), 29-49.

Khaddouma, A., Coop Gordon, K., & Strand, E. (2017). Mindful Mates: A Pilot Study of the Relational Effects of Mindfulness Based Stress Reduction on Participants and Their Partners. Family Process, 56(3), 636-651.

123 Gilbert, P. (2020). The Evolution of Pro-social Behavior: From Caring to Compassion. In Workman, L., Reader, W., & Barkow, J. H. (Eds.). The Cambridge handbook of evolutionary perspectives on human behavior. Cambridge University Press.

124 Khoury, B. (2019). Compassion: embodied and embedded. Mindfulness, 10(11), 2363-2374.

125 Klimecki, O. M., Leiberg, S., Ricard, M., & Singer, T. (2014). Differential pattern of functional brain plasticity after compassion and empathy training. Social cognitive and affective neuroscience, 9(6), 873-879.

Preckel, K., Kanske, P., & Singer, T. (2018). On the interaction of social affect and cognition: empathy, compassion and theory of mind. Current Opinion in Behavioral Sciences, 19, 1-6.

126 Neff, D. K. (2021). Fierce Self-Compassion: How Women Can Harness Kindness to Speak Up, Claim Their Power, and Thrive. Penguin UK.

127 Klimecki, O. and Singer, T. (2012). Empathic distress fatigue rather than compassion fatigue? Integrating findings from empathy research in psychology and social neuroscience. In: Oakley, A. Knafo, G. Madhaven and D. Wilson (Eds.). Pathalogical Altruism. New York: Oxford University Press.

128 Kirby, J. N., Tellegen, C. L., & Steindl, S. R. (2017). A meta-analysis of compassion-based interventions: Current state of knowledge and future directions. Behavior Therapy, 48(6), 778-792.

129 Ibid. See also:

J.L. Dickinson, P. McLeod, R. Bloomfield, S. Allred. (2016) Which moral foundations predict willingness to make lifestyle changes to avert climate change in the USA? PLoS One, 11 (10). Article e0163852

S. Pfattheicher, C. Sassenrath, S. Schindler. (2016). Feelings for the suffering of others and the environment: compassion fosters proenvironmental tendencies Environ. Behav., 48 (7)

Leiberg, S., Klimecki, O., & Singer, T. (2011). Short-term compassion training increases prosocial behavior in a newly developed prosocial game. PloS one, 6(3), e17798.

Batson 2010; de Waal 2008; Eisenberg 2000; Haidt 2003b; Hoffman 1975; Tangney et al. 2007, Davis & Oathout 1987. [DRAFTING NOTE - unpack these]

130 Trautwein, F.-M., Kanske, P., Böckler, A., & Singer, T. (2020). Differential benefits of mental training types for attention, compassion, and theory of mind. Cognition, 194(July 2019), 104039. https://doi.org/10.1016/j.cognition.2019.104039.

Wamsler, C. (2018) Mind the gap: The role of mindfulness in adapting to increasing risk and climate change. Sustainability Science, 13(4), 1121-1135.

131 López, A., Sanderman, R., Ranchor, A., & Schroevers, M. (2017). Compassion for Others and Self-Compassion: Levels, Correlates, and Relationship with Psychological Well-being. Mindfulness, 9(1), 325-331.

132 Held, P. and Owens, G.P. (2015). Effects of self-compassion workbook training on trauma-related guilt in a sample of homeless veterans: a pilot study. Journal of Clinical Psychology, 71(6), pp. 513-526

133 Kirby, J. N., Tellegen, C. L., & Steindl, S. R. (2017). A meta-analysis of compassion-based interventions: Current state of knowledge and future directions. Behavior Therapy, 48(6),)

134 Kirby, J. N., Tellegen, C. L., & Steindl, S. R. (2017). A meta-analysis of compassion-based interventions: Current state of knowledge and future directions. Behavior Therapy, 48(6),)

135   Luberto, C. M., Shinday, N., Song, R., Philpotts, L. L., Park, E. R., Fricchione, G. L., & Yeh, G. Y. (2018). A systematic review and meta-analysis of the effects of meditation on empathy, compassion, and prosocial behaviors. Mindfulness, 9(3), 708-724.

136   Walsh, Z., Böhme, J., Lavelle, B. D and Wamsler, C. (2020) Transformative education: towards a relational, justice-oriented approach to sustainability, International Journal of Sustainability in Higher Education, 21(7):1587-1606.

137   Lent, J. (2021). The Web of Meaning: Integrating Science and Traditional Wisdom to Find Our Place in the Universe. New Society Publishers.

138   Wamsler, C., Bristow, J. (2022) At the intersection of mind and climate: Integrating inner dimensions of climate change into policymaking, forthcoming.

139   Norgaard, K. M. (2006). "people want to protect themselves a little bit": Emotions, denial, and social movement nonparticipation. Sociological Inquiry, 76(3), 372–396.

        Andrews, N., & Hoggett, P. (2019). Facing up to ecological crisis: A psychosocial perspective from climate psychology. Facing up to Climate Reality: Honesty, Disaster and Hope; Foster, J. , Ed, 155–171.

140   Climate Psychology Alliance. (2008). The Climate Psychology Handbook. Retrieved (September, 2021) from Climate Psychology Alliance website: https://www.climatepsychologyalliance.org/handbook/304-coping-and-defences

141   Doering, L. V., Dracup, K., Caldwell, M. A., Moser, D. K., Erickson, V. S., Fonarow, G., & Hamilton, M. (2004). Is coping style linked to emotional states in heart failure patients?. Journal of cardiac failure, 10(4), 344-349.

        Dijkstra, M., & Homan, A. C. (2016). Engaging in rather than disengaging from stress: Effective coping and perceived control. Frontiers in psychology, 7, 1415.

142   Extinction Rebellion. (n.d.). Guide to the Impossible. Retrieved from Extinction Rebellion website: https://extinctionrebellion.uk/wp-content/uploads/2020/05/XR-GUIDE-TO-THE-IMPOSSIBLE.pdf

143   Olympic gold medallist Etienne Stott (2014). Retreived from huffingtonpost.co.uk/vogue-uk/voguearianna-

        Huffington-headspace_b_5418740.html Fraher, AL., Branicki, LJ., Grint, K. (2017). Mindfulness in Action: Discovering How U.S. Navy Seals Build Capacity for Mindfulness in High-Reliability Organizations (HROs). AMD, 3, 239–261, https://doi.org/10.5465/amd.2014.0146

144   Hafenbrack, A., Kinias, Z., & Barsade, S. (2014). Debiasing the Mind Through Meditation. Psychological Science, 25(2), 369-376.

145   Jury, T., & Jose, P. (2018). Does Rumination Function as a Longitudinal Mediator Between Mindfulness and Depression?. Mindfulness, 10(6), 1091-1104.

146   Leonard, M., (2019). Social Mindfulness: A guide to meditations from Mindfulness-Based Organisational Education. Mindfulness Connected Limited. Oxford, UK.

        Barker, MJ., (2015). Social Mindfulness. Retrieved from: https://rewriting-the-rules.com/wp-content/uploads/2015/07/socialmindfulnesszine.pdf

147   Wamsler, C., Brossmann, J., Hendersson, H., Kristjansdottir, R., McDonald, C. and Scarampi, P. (2018) Mindfulness in sustainability science, practice, and teaching, Sustainability Science, 13(1):143-162. Online.

148   Macy, J., & Brown, M. Y. (1998). Coming back to life: Practices to reconnect our lives, our world. Gabriola Island, BC: New Society.

149   Macy, J. (2007). World as lover, world as self: Courage for global justice and ecological renewal. Berkeley, CA: Parallax Press

150   Johnstone, C., 2002. Reconnecting with our world. In: A. Chesner and H. Hahn, eds. 2002. Creative Advances in Groupwork. London: Jessica Kingsley Publishers. Ch. 8, pp.186 - 216.

151   Hathaway, M. D., 2017. Activating Hope in the Midst of Crisis: Emotions, Transformative Learning, and "The Work That Reconnects". Journal of Transformative Education, 15(4), pp. 296–314. https://doi.org/10.1177/1541344616680350.

Hollis-Walker L., 2012. Change Processes in Emotion-Focused Therapy and the Work That Reconnects. Ecopsychology, 4(1), pp.25- 36.

152   Hickman, C., Marks, E., Pihkala, P., Clayton, S., Lewandowski, R. E., Mayall, E. E., ... & van Susteren, L. (2021). Climate anxiety in children and young people and their beliefs about government responses to climate change: a global survey. The Lancet Planetary Health, 5(12), e863-e873.

153   Wamsler, C., Bristow, J. (2022) At the intersection of mind and climate: Integrating inner dimensions of climate change into policymaking, forthcoming.

154   Macy, J., & Johnstone, C. (2012). Active Hope: How to Face the Mess We're in Without Going Crazy. New World Library.

155   Wamsler, C., Bristow, J. (2022) At the intersection of mind and climate: Integrating inner dimensions of climate change into policymaking, forthcoming.

156   Fisher, D. M., Ragsdale, J. M., & Fisher, E. C. (2018). The importance of definitional and temporal issues in the study of resilience. Applied Psychology: An International Review. Advance online publication. http://dx.doi.org/10.1111/apps.12162

Van Breda, A. D. (2018). A critical review of resilience theory and its relevance for social work. Social Work, 54, 1-18. http://dx.doi.org/10.15270/54-1-611

157   Wamsler C., Reeder L., Crosweller M. (2020) The being of urban resilience. In: Handbook of Urban Resilience, Burayidi, M., Allen, A., Twigg, J., Wamsler, C. (Eds.), Routledge. Online.

Wamsler, C., Bristow, J. (2022) At the intersection of mind and climate: Integrating inner dimensions of climate change into policymaking, forthcoming.

158   Joyce, S., Shand, F., Tighe, J., Laurent, S. J., Bryant, R. A., & Harvey, S. B. (2018). Road to resilience: a systematic review and meta-analysis of resilience training programmes and interventions. BMJ open, 8(6), e017858.

Lefebvre, J., Montani, F., & Courcy, F. (2020). Self-Compassion and Resilience at Work: A Practice-Oriented Review. Advances in Developing Human Resources, 22(4), 437-452.
Angelopoulou, P., & Panagopoulou, E. (2022). Resilience interventions in physicians: A systematic review and meta analysis. Applied Psychology: Health and Well-Being, 14(1), 3-25.

159   Iani, L., Lauriola, M., Chiesa, A., & Cafaro, V. (2018). Associations Between Mindfulness and Emotion Regulation: the Key Role of Describing and Nonreactivity. Mindfulness, 10(2), 366-375.

Inwood, E., & Ferrari, M. (2018). Mechanisms of change in the relationship between self compassion, emotion regulation, and mental health: A systematic review. Applied Psychology: Health and Well Being, 10(2), 215-235.

160   Gilbert, P., & Irons, C. (2009). Shame, self-criticism, and self-compassion in adolescence. Adolescent emotional development and the emergence of depressive disorders, 1, 195-214.

Held, P. and Owens, G.P. (2015). Effects of self-compassion workbook training on trauma-related guilt in a sample of homeless veterans: a pilot study. Journal of Clinical Psychology, 71(6), pp. 513-526

Eaton, E., Capone, C., Shea, M. T., & Cameron, A. (2020). Evaluation of self-compassion focused group treatment for co-occurring PTSD and substance use inveterans with posttraumatic guilt: A case study. International Journal of GroupPsychotherapy,70(4), 481–508

161   Flanagan, O. (2013). The shame of addiction. Frontiers in Psychiatry, 4, 120. Duarte, C., Matos, M., Stubbs, R., Gale, C., Morris, L., Gouveia, J., & Gilbert, P. (2017). The Impact of Shame, Self-Criticism and Social Rank on Eating Behaviours in Overweight and Obese Women Participating in a Weight Management Programme. PLoS ONE, 12(1),

162   Goldberg, SB., Tucker, RP.,Greene, PA., Davidson, RJ., Wampold, BE., Kearney, DJ., Simpson, TL. (2018) Mindfulness-based interventions for psychiatric disorders: A systematic review and meta-analysis. Clin Psychol Rev. 2018 Feb; 59: 52–60.

        Khoury, B., Sharmac, M., Rush, SE., Fourniere, C., (2015). Mindfulness-based stress reduction for healthy individuals: A meta-analysis. Journal of Psychosomatic Research. 78.6:519-528 Jayawardene, W., Lohrmann, D., Erbe, R., & Torabi, M. (2016). Effects of preventive online mindfulness interventions on stress and mindfulness: A meta-analysis of randomized controlled trials. Preventive Medicine Reports, 5, 150-159.

163   Jha, A., Morrison, A., Parker, S., & Stanley, E. (2016). Practice Is Protective: Mindfulness Training Promotes Cognitive Resilience in High-Stress Cohorts. Mindfulness, 8(1), 46-58.

164   Jha, A., Morrison, A., Parker, S., & Stanley, E. (2016). Practice Is Protective: Mindfulness Training Promotes Cognitive Resilience in High-Stress Cohorts. Mindfulness, 8(1), 46-58.

        Jha, A., Zanesco, A., Denkova, E., Morrison, A., Ramos, N., Chichester, K., Gaddy, J., & Rogers, S. (2020). Bolstering Cognitive Resilience via Train-the-Trainer Delivery of Mindfulness Training in Applied High-Demand Settings. Mindfulness, 11(3), 683-697.

        Cásedas, L., Pirruccio, V., Vadillo, M., & Lupiáñez, J. (2020). Does Mindfulness Meditation Training Enhance Executive Control? A Systematic Review and Meta-Analysis of Randomized Controlled Trials in Adults. Mindfulness, 11(2), 411-424.

165   Jha, A., Witkin, J., Morrison, A., Rostrup, N., & Stanley, E. (2017). Short-Form Mindfulness Training Protects Against Working Memory Degradation over High-Demand Intervals. Journal of Cognitive Enhancement, 1(2), 154-171.

166   Gorski, P. (2015). Relieving Burnout and the "Martyr Syndrome" Among Social Justice Education Activists: The Implications and Effects of Mindfulness. The Urban Review, 47(4), 696-716.

        Driscoll, D. (2020). When Ignoring the News and Going Hiking Can Help You Save the World: Environmental Activist Strategies for Persistence. Sociological Forum, 35(1), 189-206.

167   Tugade, M., & Fredrickson, B. (2004). Resilient Individuals Use Positive Emotions to Bounce Back From Negative Emotional Experiences. Journal of Personality and Social Psychology, 86(2), 320-333.

168   Fredrickson, B. L. (2013). Positive emotions broaden and build. In Advances in experimental social psychology (Vol. 47, pp. 1-53). Academic Press.

169   Wamsler, C., Brossmann, J., Hendersson, H., Kristjansdottir, R., McDonald, C. and Scarampi, P. (2018) Mindfulness in sustainability science, practice, and teaching, Sustainability Science, 13(1):143-162. Online.

        Kushlev, K., Drummond, D. M., Heintzelman, S. J., & Diener, E. (2020). Do happy people care about society's problems?. The Journal of Positive Psychology, 15(4), 467-477.

170   Barsade, S. G. (2002). The ripple effect: Emotional contagion and its influence on group behavior. Administrative science quarterly, 47(4), 644-675.

171   E.g. Regeneration - Paul Hawken; Climate: A New Story by Charles Eisenstein.

172   Wood, A. M., Froh, J. J., & Geraghty, A. W. (2010). Gratitude and well-being: A review and theoretical integration. *Clinical psychology review*, 30(7), 890-905.

173   Yost-Dubrow, R., & Dunham, Y. (2018). Evidence for a relationship between trait gratitude and prosocial behaviour. Cognition and Emotion, 32(2), 397-403.

        Aknin, L. B., Van de Vondervoort, J. W., & Hamlin, J. K. (2018). Positive feelings reward and promote prosocial behavior. Current opinion in psychology, 20, 55-59.

174   Stellar, J., Gordon, A., Piff, P., Cordaro, D., Anderson, C., Bai, Y., Maruskin, L., & Keltner, D. (2017). Self-Transcendent Emotions and Their Social Functions: Compassion, Gratitude, and Awe Bind Us to Others Through Prosociality. Emotion Review, 9(3), 200-207.

175   Macy, J., & Johnstone, C. (2012). Active hope: How to face the mess we're in without going crazy. Novato, CA: New World Library

176   TED Countdown (Producer). (2020, October 23). Christiana Figueres: The case for stubborn optimism on climate [Video file]. Retrieved from https://racetozero.unfccc.int/christiana-figueres-the-case-for-stubborn-optimism-on-climate/

177   Schumer, M. C., Lindsay, E. K., & Creswell, J. D. (2018). Brief mindfulness training for negative affectivity: A systematic review and meta-analysis. Journal of Consulting and Clinical Psychology, 86(7), 569.

        Leyland, A., Rowse, G., & Emerson, L. M. (2019). Experimental effects of mindfulness inductions on self-regulation: Systematic review and meta-analysis. Emotion, 19(1), 108.

178   Garland, E. L., Geschwind, N., Peeters, F., & Wichers, M. (2015). Mindfulness training promotes upward spirals of positive affect and cognition: multilevel and autoregressive latent trajectory modeling analyses. Frontiers in psychology, 6, 15.

179   Garland, E. L., Farb, N. A., R. Goldin, P., & Fredrickson, B. L. (2015). Mindfulness broadens awareness and builds eudaimonic meaning: A process model of mindful positive emotion regulation. Psychological inquiry, 26(4), 293-314.

180   Tumminia, M. J., Colaianne, B. A., Roeser, R. W., & Galla, B. M. (2020). How is mindfulness linked to negative and positive affect? Rumination as an explanatory process in a prospective longitudinal study of adolescents. Journal of youth and adolescence, 49(10), 2136-2148.

        Arimitsu, K., & Hofmann, S. G. (2015). Effects of compassionate thinking on negative emotions. Cognition and Emotion, 1-8. doi:10.1080/02699931.2015.1078292

        Beshai, S., Prentice, J. L., & Huang, V. (2018). Building blocks of emotional flexibility: Trait mindfulness and self-compassion are associated with positive and negative mood shifts. Mindfulness, 9(3), 939-948.

181   Engen, H. G., & Singer, T. (2015). Compassion-based emotion regulation up-regulates experienced positive affect and associated neural networks. Social cognitive and affective neuroscience, 10(9), 1291-1301.

182   LeBlanc, S., Uzun, B., & Aydemir, A. (2021). Structural relationship among mindfulness, reappraisal and life satisfaction: The mediating role of positive affect. Current Psychology, 40(9), 4406-4415.

183   Swickert, R., Bailey, E., Hittner, J., Spector, A., Benson-Townsend, B., & Silver, N. (2018). The Mediational Roles of Gratitude and Perceived Support in Explaining the Relationship Between Mindfulness and Mood. Journal of Happiness Studies, 20(3), 815-828.

184   Schutte, N., Keng, S., & Cheung, M. (2021). Emotional Intelligence Mediates the Connection Between Mindfulness and Gratitude: a Meta-Analytic Structural Equation Modeling Study. Mindfulness, 12(11), 2613-2623.

185   Thornton, L. M., Cheavens, J. S., Heitzmann, C. A., Dorfman, C. S., Wu, S. M., & Andersen, B. L. (2014). Test of mindfulness and hope components in a psychological intervention for women with cancer recurrence. Journal of Consulting and Clinical Psychology, 82, 1087-1100. doi:100.1037/a0036959

186   Munoz, R., Hoppes, S., Hellman, C., Brunk, K., Bragg, J., & Cummins, C. (2018). The Effects of Mindfulness Meditation on Hope and Stress. Research on Social Work Practice, 28(6), 696-707.

187   Malinowski, P., & Lim, H. J. (2015). Mindfulness at work: Positive affect, hope, and optimism mediate the relationship between dispositional mindfulness, work engagement, and well-being. Mindfulness, 6(6), 1250-1262.

188   Meadows, D. (1992). Leverage Points: Places to Intervene in a System. The Sustainability Institute.

        Göpel, M. (2016). The great mindshift: how a new economic paradigm and sustainability transformations go hand in hand. Springer Nature.

        Fischer, J. and M. Riechers, 2019: A leverage points perspective on sustainability. People and Nature, 1(1), 115-120,doi:10.1002/pan3.13.

189   Ballew, M.T., Goldberg, M.H., Rosenthal, A., Gustafson, A., Leiserowitz, A. 2019. Systems thinking as a pathway to global warming beliefs and attitudes through an ecological worldview. Proceedings or the National Academy of Aciences, 116 (17) 8214-8219

        Wamsler, C., Osberg, G., Osika, W., Hendersson, H., Mundaca, L. (2021) Linking internal and external transformation for sustainability and climate action: Towards a new research and policy agenda, Global Environmental Change, Volume 71, 102373.

190   Woiwode, C., Schäpke, N., Bina, O., Veciana, S., Kunze, I., Parodi, O., Schweizer-Ries, P., & Wamsler, C. (2021). Inner transformation to sustainability as a deep leverage point: fostering new avenues for change through dialogue and reflection. Sustainability Science, 16(3), 841-858.

191   Lent, J. (2017). The Patterning Instinct: A Cultural History of Humanity's Search for Meaning. Prometheus Books

192   Hanh, T. N. (1997). Interbeing. RESURGENCE-LONDON-NAVERN ROAD-, 42-43.

193   Mackay, C. M. L., & Schmitt, M. T. (2019). Do people who feel connected to nature do more to protect it? A meta-analysis. Journal of Environmental Psychology, 65, 101323.

        Schmitt, M. T., Mackay, C. M. L., Droogendyk, L. M., & Payne, D. (2019). What predicts environmental activism? The roles of identification with nature and politicized environmental identity. Journal of Environmental Psychology, 61, 20–29.

194   Siegel, D. (2022). IntraConnected: MWe (Me + We) As the Integration of Self, Identity, and Belonging. W. W. Norton & Company. Forthcoming.

195   Siegel, D. (2022). IntraConnected: MWe (Me + We) As the Integration of Self, Identity, and Belonging. W. W. Norton & Company. Forthcoming.

196   Kirk, U., Brown, K., & Downar, J. (2015). Adaptive neural reward processing during anticipation and receipt of monetary rewards in mindfulness meditators. Social Cognitive and Affective Neuroscience, 10(5), 752-759.

        Kashdan, T. B., Afram, A., Brown, K. W., Birnbeck, M., & Drvoshanov, M. (2011). Curiosity enhances the role of mindfulness in reducing defensive responses to existential threat. Personality and Individual Differences, 50(8), 1227-1232.

197   Wamsler, C. (2018) Mind the gap: The role of mindfulness in adapting to increasing risk and climate change. Sustainability Science, 13(4), 1121-1135. Online.

        Wamsler, C., Brink, E. (2018) Mindsets for sustainability: Exploring the link between mindfulness and sustainable climate adaptation, Ecological Economics, 151:55-61. Online.

        Ramstetter, L., Rupprecht, S., Mundaca, L., Klackl, J., Osika, W., Stenfors, C., Wamsler, C. (2022) Fostering (collective) climate action and leadership: Insights from a pilot experiment with a 10-week behavioral intervention involving mindfulness and compassion. (forthcoming).

198   Jonas, E., McGregor, I., Klackl, J., Agroskin, D., Fritsche, I., Holbrook, C., ... & Quirin, M. (2014). Threat and defense: From anxiety to approach. In Advances in experimental social psychology (Vol. 49, pp. 219-286). Academic Press.

199   Bernstein, A., Hadash, Y., & Fresco, D. M. (2019). Metacognitive processes model of decentering: Emerging methods and insights. Current Opinion in Psychology, 28, 245-251.

200   Edwards, M., (2020). The road beyond McMindfulness: What can we learn from 22 articles on mindfulness and social change? openDemocracy. Retrieved from: https://www.opendemocracy.net/en/transformation/road-beyond-mcmindfulness/

201   Barnard, P. J., & Teasdale, J. D. (1991). Interacting cognitive subsystems: A systemic approach to cognitive-affective interaction and change. Cognition & Emotion, 5(1), 1-39.
        Teasdale, J. D., & Chaskalson, M. (2011). How does mindfulness transform suffering? II: the transformation of dukkha. Contemporary Buddhism, 12(1), 103-124.

202   Ibid.

203   Yama, H., Zakaria, N. (2019). Explanations for cultural differences in thinking: Easterners' dialectical thinking and Westerners' linear thinking Journal of Cognitive Psychology. 31(4); 487-506. https://doi.org/10.1080/20445911.2019.1626862.

204   McGilchrist, I. (2012). The Master and His Emissary. Yale University Press; 2nd edition.

205   McGilchrist, I. (2021, November 17). The Matter With Things, Iain McGilchrist [Video file]. Retrieved from https://www.youtube.com/watch?v=U99dQrZdVTg

206   Livingstone, L. (2019). Taking sustainability to heart––towards engaging with sustainability issues through heart-centred thinking. In Sustainability and the Humanities (pp. 455-467). Springer, Cham.

207   Reiljan, A. (2020). 'Fear and loathing across party lines'(also) in Europe: Affective polarisation in European party systems. European journal of political research, 59(2), 376-396.

208   Sikder, O., Smith, R., Vivo, P., & Livan, G. (2020). A minimalistic model of bias, polarization and misinformation in social networks. Scientific Reports, 10, 10(1), 1-11.

209   Druckman, J. N., Klar, S., Krupnikov, Y., Levendusky, M., & Ryan, J. B. (2021). Affective polarization, local contexts and public opinion in America. Nature human behaviour, 5(1), 28-38.

210   Clark, A., Justwan, F., Carlisle, J. E., & Clark, M. (2020). Polarization politics and hopes for a green agenda in the United States. Environmental Politics, 29(4), 719-745.

Dunlap, R. E., McCright, A. M., & Yarosh, J. H. (2016). The political divide on climate change: Partisan polarization widens in the US. Environment: Science and Policy for Sustainable Development, 58(5), 4-23.

McCright, A. M., Dunlap, R. E., & Marquart-Pyatt, S. T. (2016). Political ideology and views about climate change in the European Union. Environmental Politics, 25(2), 338-358.

211   Adam A. Kaya, A.A., Skarlicki, D.P., (2017). Cultivating a conflict-positive workplace: How mindfulness facilitates constructive conflict management. Organizational Behavior and Human Decision Processes journal homepage: www.elsevier.com/locate/obhdp

212   Zmigrod, L., Zmigrod, S., Rentfrow, P. J., & Robbins, T. W. (2019). The psychological roots of intellectual humility: The role of intelligence and cognitive flexibility. Personality and Individual Differences, 141, 200-208.

Zmigrod, L., Rentfrow, P. J., & Robbins, T. W. (2020). The partisan mind: Is extreme political partisanship related to cognitive inflexibility?. Journal of Experimental Psychology: General, 149(3), 407.

213   Simonsson, O. (2020). Meditative practices-correlates and consequences for political attitudes (Doctoral dissertation, University of Oxford).

Simonsson, O., Narayanan, J., & Marks, J. (2021). Love thy (partisan) neighbor: Brief befriending meditation reduces affective polarization. Group Processes & Intergroup Relations, 13684302211020108.

Simonsson, O., Bazin, O., Fisher, S. D., & Goldberg, S. B. (2022). Effects of an 8-Week Mindfulness Course on Affective Polarization. Mindfulness, 1-10.

214   Alkoby, A., Halperin, E., Tarrasch, R., & Levit-Binnun, N. (2017). Increased support for political compromise in the Israeli-Palestinian conflict following an 8-week mindfulness workshop. Mindfulness, 8(5), 1345-1353.

215   Ives, C. D., Abson, D. J., Von Wehrden, H., Dorninger, C., Klaniecki, K., & Fischer, J. (2018). Reconnecting with nature for sustainability. Sustainability science, 13(5), 1389-1397.

216   Connection to nature. (n.d.). Retrieved Feb 23, 2022, from RSPB website: https://www.rspb.org.uk/our-work/conservation/projects/connection-to-nature/

217   Natural England. (2020). A summary report on nature connectedness among adults and children in England Analyses of relationships with wellbeing and pro-environmental behaviours.Retrieved from Natural England website: http://publications.naturalengland.org.uk/publication/6005041314136064

218   Otto, S., & Pensini, P. (2017). Nature-based environmental education of children: Environmental knowledge and connectedness to nature, together, are related to ecological behaviour. Global Environmental Change, 47, 88-94.

Weinstein, N., Przybylski, A. K., & Ryan, R. M. (2009). Can nature make us more caring? Effects of immersion in nature on intrinsic aspirations and generosity. Personality & Social Psychology Bulletin, 35(10), 1315–1329.

219   Lumber, R., Richardson, M. and Sheffield, D., 2017. Beyond knowing nature: Contact, emotion, compassion, meaning, and beauty are pathways to nature connection. PloS one, 12(5), p.e0177186.

220   Lumber R, Richardson M, Sheffield D (2017) Beyond knowing nature: Contact, emotion, compassion, meaning, and beauty are pathways to nature connection. PLoS ONE 12(5): e0177186. https://doi.org/10.1371/journal.pone.0177186

221   Schutte, N. S., & Malouff, J. M. (2018). Mindfulness and connectedness to nature: A meta-analytic investigation. Personality and Individual Differences, 127, 10-14.

222   Howell, A.J., Dopko, R.L., Passmore, H.A. and Buro, K., 2011. Nature connectedness: Associations with well-being and mindfulness. Personality and individual differences, 51(2), pp.166-171.

        Wolsko, C., & Lindberg, K. (2013). Experiencing connection with nature: The matrix of psychological well-being, mindfulness, and outdoor recreation. Ecopsychology, 5(2), 80-91.

223   Farkić, J., Filep, S., & Taylor, S. (2020). Shaping tourists' wellbeing through guided slow adventures. Journal of Sustainable Tourism, 28(12), 2064-2080.

        Nisbet, E. K., Zelenski, J. M., & Grandpierre, Z. (2019). Mindfulness in nature enhances connectedness and mood. Ecopsychology, 11(2), 81-91.

224   Kurth, A. M., Narvaez, D., Kohn, R., & Bae, A. (2020). Indigenous Nature Connection: A 3-Week Intervention Increased Ecological Attachment. Ecopsychology, 12(2), 101-117.

        Ramstetter, L., Rupprecht, S., Mundaca, L., Klackl, J., Osika, W., Stenfors, C., Wamsler, C. (2022) Fostering (collective) climate action and leadership: Insights from a pilot experiment with a 10-week behavioral intervention involving mindfulness and compassion. (forthcoming).

225   The right to a clean, healthy and sustainable environment: non-toxic environment: Report of the Special Rapporteur on the issue of human rights obligations relating to the enjoyment of a safe, clean, healthy and sustainable environment, presented to the United Nations General Assembly Human Rights Council Forty-ninth session 28 February–1 April 2022 Agenda item 3 https://documents-dds-ny.un.org/doc/UNDOC/GEN/G22/004/48/PDF/G2200448.pdf?OpenElement

        See also Interview with Robert Bullard: Environmental justice isn't just slang: it's real by Oliver Milman https://www.theguardian.com/commentisfree/2018/dec/20/robert-bullard-interview-environmental-justice-civil-rights-movement

226   IPCC, 2022: Climate Change 2022: Mitigation of Climate Change. Contribution of Working Group III to the Sixth Assessment Report of the Intergovernmental Panel on Climate Change [P.R. Shukla, J. Skea, R. Slade, A. Al Khourdajie, R. van Diemen, D. McCollum, M. Pathak, S. Some, P. Vyas, R. Fradera, M. Belkacemi, A. Hasija, G. Lisboa, S. Luz, J. Malley, (eds.)]. Cambridge University Press, Cambridge, UK and New York, NY, USA. doi: 10.1017/9781009157926

227   Godin, G., Conner, M., & Sheeran, P. (2005). Bridging the intention–behaviour gap: The role of moral norm. British journal of social psychology, 44(4), 497-512.

228   Overconsumption and the environment: should we all stop shopping? (2021, May 30), The Guardian. Retrieved from https://www.theguardian.com/lifeandstyle/2021/may/30/should-we-all-stop-shopping-how-to-end-overconsumption

229   Clear signs of global warming will hit poorer countries first (2018, April 20), Nature. Retrieved from https://www.nature.com/articles/d41586-018-04854-2

230   GDP and life satisfaction: New evidence (2013, January 11). Vox EU. Retrieved from: https://voxeu.org/article/gdp-and-life-satisfaction-new-evidence

231   Fischer, D., Stanszus, L., Geiger, S., Grossman, P., & Schrader, U. (2017). Mindfulness and Sustainable Consumption: A Systematic Literature Review of Research Approaches and Findings. Journal of Cleaner Production, 162, 544–558. https://doi.org/10.1016/j.jclepro.2017.06.007

        Geiger, S. M., Grossman, P., & Schrader, U. (2018). Mindfulness and sustainability: Correlation or causation? Current Opinion in Psychology, 28, 23–27. https://doi.org/10.1016/j.copsyc.2018.09.010

        Geiger, S. M., & Keller, J. (2018). Shopping for Clothes and Sensitivity to the Suffering of Others: The Role of Compassion and Values in Sustainable Fashion Consumption: The Role of Compassion and Values in Sustainable Fashion Consumption. Environment and Behavior, 50(10), 1119–1144. https://doi.org/10.1177/0013916517732109

232   Edwards, M., (2020). The road beyond McMindfulness: What can we learn from 22 articles on mindfulness and social change? openDemocracy. Retrieved from: https://www.opendemocracy.net/en/transformation/road-beyond-mcmindfulness/

233   Liang, J., & Guo, L. (2021). Gratitude and sustainable consumer behavior: A moderated mediation model of time discounting and connectedness to the future self. Psychology & Marketing, 38(8), 1238-1249.

234   Geiger, S. M., & Keller, J. (2018). Shopping for Clothes and Sensitivity to the Suffering of Others: The Role of Compassion and Values in Sustainable Fashion Consumption: The Role of Compassion and Values in Sustainable Fashion Consumption. Environment and Behavior, 50(10), 1119–1144. https://doi.org/10.1177/0013916517732109

235   Frank, P., Stanszus, L., Fischer, D., Grossman, P., & Schrader, U. (2021, under review). What happens when people start to meditate on consumption? An explorative study inquiring into the potential of mindfulness practice for environmental and sustainability education. Journal of Environmental Education.

236   Thiermann, U., & Sheate, W. (2020). The Way Forward in Mindfulness and Sustainability: a Critical Review and Research Agenda. Journal of Cognitive Enhancement, 5(1), 118-139.

237   Holmes, T., Blackmore, E., Hawkins, R., Wakeford, T., (2011). The Common Cause Handbook. Public Interest Research Centre. Machynlleth, Wales.

238   Geiger, S. M., Fischer, D., Schrader, U., & Grossman, P. (2020). Meditating for the Planet: Effects of a Mindfulness-Based Intervention on Sustainable Consumption Behaviors. Environment and Behavior, 52(9), 1012–1042. https://doi.org/10.1177/0013916519880897

        Geiger, S. M., Grossman, P., & Schrader, U. (2018). Mindfulness and sustainability: Correlation or causation? Current Opinion in Psychology, 28, 23–27. https://doi.org/10.1016/j.copsyc.2018.09.010

239   Bristow, J., Bell, R., Nixon, D. (2020). Mindfulness: developing agency in urgent times.The Mindfulness Initiative. https://www.themindfulnessinitiative.org/agency-in-urgent-times/

240   Holmes, T., Blackmore, E., Hawkins, R., Wakeford, T., (2011). The Common Cause Handbook. Public Interest Research Centre. Machynlleth, Wales.

241   Ibid.

242   Ibid.

243   Shonin, E., & Gordon, W. (2016). The Mechanisms of Mindfulness in the Treatment of Mental Illness and Addiction. International Journal of Mental Health and Addiction, 14(5), 844-849.

244   Hayes, S., Pistorello, J., & Levin, M. (2012). Acceptance and Commitment Therapy as a Unified Model of Behavior Change. The Counseling Psychologist, 40(7), 976-1002.

        Manlick, C., Cochran, S., & Koon, J. (2012). Acceptance and Commitment Therapy for Eating Disorders: Rationale and Literature Review. Journal of Contemporary Psychotherapy, 43(2), 115-122.

        Vowles, K.E., Wetherell, J.L., Sorrell, J.T., (2009) Targeting Acceptance, Mindfulness, and Values-Based Action in Chronic Pain: Findings of Two Preliminary Trials of an Outpatient Group-Based Intervention. Cognitive and Behavioral Practice 16 (2009) 49–58

245   Frank, P., Stanszus, L., Fischer, D., Grossman, P., & Schrader, U. (2021, under review). What happens when people start to meditate on consumption? An explorative study inquiring into the potential of mindfulness practice for environmental and sustainability education. Journal of Environmental Education.

        Frank, P., Sundermann, A., & Fischer, D. (2019). How mindfulness training cultivates introspection and competence development for sustainable consumption. International Journal of Sustainability in Higher Education, 20(6), 1002–1021. https://doi.org/10.1108/IJSHE-12-2018-0239
        Geiger, S. M., & Keller, J. (2018). Shopping for Clothes and Sensitivity to the Suffering of Others: The Role of Compassion and Values in Sustainable Fashion Consumption: The Role of Compassion and Values in Sustainable Fashion Consumption. Environment and Behavior, 50(10), 1119–1144. https://doi.org/10.1177/0013916517732109

246   L. Steg and C. Vlek, "Encouraging pro-environmental behaviour: An integrative review and research agenda," J. Environ. Psychol., vol. 29, no. 3, pp. 309–317, 2009.

247   U. B. Thiermann and W. R. Sheate, "The Way Forward in Mindfulness and Sustainability: a Critical Review and Research Agenda," J. Cogn. Enhanc., Jul. 2020.

248   D. Fischer, L. S. Stanszus, S. M. Geiger, P. Grossman, and U. Schrader, "Mindfulness and sustainable consumption: A systematic literature review of research approaches and findings," J. Clean. Prod., vol. 162, pp. 544–558, 2017.

T. K. Dhandra, "Achieving triple dividend through mindfulness: More sustainable consumption, less unsustainable consumption and more life satisfaction," Ecol. Econ., vol. 161, no. March, pp. 83–90, 2019.

A. Werner, A. Spiller, and S. G. H. Meyerding, "The yoga of sustainable diets : Exploring consumers mind and spirit," J. Clean. Prod., vol. 243, p. 118473, 2020.

M. Hunecke and N. Richter, "Mindfulness, Construction of Meaning, and Sustainable Food Consumption," Mindfulness (N. Y)., vol. 10, no. 3, pp. 446–458, 2019.

249   L. S. Loy and G. Reese, "Hype and hope? Mind-body practice predicts pro-environmental engagement through global identity," J. Environ. Psychol., vol. 66, no. August, p. 101340, 2019.

A. Panno, M. Giacomantonio, G. Carrus, F. Maricchiolo, S. Pirchio, and L. Mannetti, "Mindfulness, Pro-environmental Behavior, and Belief in Climate Change: The Mediating Role of Social Dominance," Environ. Behav., vol. 50, no. 8, pp. 864–888, Oct. 2018.

J. Jacob, E. Jovic, and M. B. Brinkerhoff, "Personal and planetary well-being: Mindfulness meditation, pro-environmental behavior and personal quality of life in a survey from the social justice and ecological sustainability movement," Soc. Indic. Res., vol. 93, no. 2, pp. 275–294, 2009.

U. B. Thiermann, W. R. Sheate, and A. Vercammen, "Practice Matters: Pro-environmental Motivations and Diet-Related Impact Vary With Meditation Experience," Front. Psychol., vol. 11, no. December, pp. 1–18, Dec. 2020.

250   U. B. Thiermann and W. R. Sheate, "Motivating individuals for social transition: The 2-pathway model and experiential strategies for pro-environmental behaviour," Ecol. Econ., vol. 174, p. 106668, Aug. 2020.

251   U. B. Thiermann, W. R. Sheate, and A. Vercammen, "Practice Matters: Pro-environmental Motivations and Diet-Related Impact Vary With Meditation Experience," Front. Psychol., vol. 11, no. December, pp. 1–18, Dec. 2020.

S. M. Geiger, P. Grossman, and U. Schrader, "Mindfulness and sustainability: correlation or causation?," Curr. Opin. Psychol., vol. 28, pp. 23–27, 2019.

252   H. J. Park and T. K. Dhandra, "Relation between dispositional mindfulness and impulsive buying tendency: Role of trait emotional intelligence," Pers. Individ. Dif., vol. 105, pp. 208–212, 2017.

A. Armstrong, "Mindfulness and consumerism: a social psychological investigation," ProQuest, 2012.

E. L. Amel, C. M. Manning, and B. a. Scott, "Mindfulness and Sustainable Behavior: Pondering Attention and Awareness as Means for Increasing Green Behavior," Ecopsychology, vol. 1, no. 1, pp. 14–25, 2009.

253   L. S. Loy and G. Reese, "Hype and hope? Mind-body practice predicts pro-environmental engagement through global identity," J. Environ. Psychol., vol. 66, no. August, p. 101340, 2019.

A. Panno, M. Giacomantonio, G. Carrus, F. Maricchiolo, S. Pirchio, and L. Mannetti, "Mindfulness, Pro-environmental Behavior, and Belief in Climate Change: The Mediating Role of Social Dominance," Environ. Behav., vol. 50, no. 8, pp. 864–888, Oct. 2018.

254   N. S. Schutte and J. M. Malouff, "Mindfulness and connectedness to nature: A meta-analytic investigation," Pers. Individ. Dif., vol. 127, no. February, pp. 10–14, 2018.

S. A. Deringer, A. Hanley, J. Hodges, and L. K. Griffin, "Improving Ecological Behavior in Outdoor Recreation Through Mindfulness Interventions: A Mixed Methods Inquiry," J. Outdoor Recreat. Educ. Leadersh., vol. 12, no. 2, pp. 149–163, 2020.

N. Barbaro and S. M. Pickett, "Mindfully green: Examining the effect of connectedness to nature on the relationship between mindfulness and engagement in pro-environmental behavior," Pers. Individ. Dif., vol. 93, pp. 137–142, 2016.

255   T. K. Dhandra, "Achieving triple dividend through mindfulness: More sustainable consumption, less unsustainable consumption and more life satisfaction," Ecol. Econ., vol. 161, no. March, pp. 83–90, 2019.

      M. Giacomantonio, V. De Cristofaro, A. Panno, V. Pellegrini, M. Salvati, and L. Leone, "The mindful way out of materialism: Mindfulness mediates the association between regulatory modes and materialism," Curr. Psychol., 2020.

256   A. Franquesa et al., "Meditation Practice Is Associated with a Values-Oriented Life: the Mediating Role of Decentering and Mindfulness," Mindfulness (N. Y)., vol. 8, no. 5, pp. 1259–1268, 2017.

257   T. K. Dhandra, "Achieving triple dividend through mindfulness: More sustainable consumption, less unsustainable consumption and more life satisfaction," Ecol. Econ., vol. 161, no. March, pp. 83–90, 2019.

      J. Jacob, E. Jovic, and M. B. Brinkerhoff, "Personal and planetary well-being: Mindfulness meditation, pro-environmental behavior and personal quality of life in a survey from the social justice and ecological sustainability movement," Soc. Indic. Res., vol. 93, no. 2, pp. 275–294, 2009.

258   S. M. Geiger, S. Otto, and U. Schrader, "Mindfully green and healthy: An indirect path from mindfulness to ecological behavior," Front. Psychol., vol. 8, no. JAN, pp. 1–11, 2018.

259   Blake, J. (1999). "Overcoming the 'value-action gap' in environmental policy: Tensions between national policy and local experience". Local Environment. 4 (3): 257–278. doi:10.1080/13549839908725599.

260   Thaler, Richard H.; Sunstein, Cass R. (April 8, 2008). Nudge: Improving Decisions about Health, Wealth, and Happiness. Yale University Press. ISBN 978-0-14-311526-7. OCLC 791403664.

261   Charles, D. (2013) The Power of Habit: Why We Do What We Do, and How to Change. Random House Books

262   Nock MK, Wedig MM, Holmberg EB, Hooley JM. (2010). The Emotion Reactivity Scale: Development, evaluation, and relation to self-injurious thoughts and behaviors. Behav Therapy. 39:107–16.

263   Killingsworth, M. A., & Gilbert, D. T. (2010). A wandering mind is an unhappy mind. Science, 330(6006), 932-932.

264   Larche, C., Tran, P., Kruger, T., Dhaliwal, N., Dixon, M., & , (2021). Escaping the Woes Through Flow? Examining the Relationship Between Escapism, Depression, and Flow Experience in Role-Playing and Platform Games. Journal of Gambling Issues, 46

      Zhang, S. Y., & Liu, L. (2013). Attention trade-off between two types of user contributions: Effects of pinterest-style infinite scroll layouts on creating original sharing and appreciating others' sharing.

265   Segal, Z. V., Williams, J. M. G., & Teasdale, J. D. (2001). Mindfulness-Based Cognitive Therapy for Depression, First Edition: A New Approach to Preventing Relapse. Guilford Publications.

266   Jury, T., & Jose, P. (2018). Does Rumination Function as a Longitudinal Mediator Between Mindfulness and Depression?. Mindfulness, 10(6), 1091-1104.

      162 Stanszus, L.S., Frank, P., Geiger, S.M., (2019). Healthy eating and sustainable nutrition through mindfulness? Mixed method results of a controlled intervention study. Appetite. 141: 104325. https://doi.org/10.1016/j.appet.2019.104325

      Warren, J., Smith, N., & Ashwell, M. (2017). A structured literature review on the role of mindfulness, mindful eating and intuitive eating in changing eating behaviours: Effectiveness and associated potential mechanisms. Nutrition Research Reviews, 30(2), 272-283. doi:10.1017/S0954422417000154

      Ostafin, B., Bauer, C., & Myxter, P. (2012). Mindfulness Decouples the Relation Between Automatic Alcohol Motivation and Heavy Drinking. Journal of Social and Clinical Psychology, 31(7), 729-745.

267   Peters, J. R., Erisman, S. M., Upton, B. T., Baer, R. A., & Roemer, L. (2011). A preliminary investigation of the relationships between dispositional mindfulness and impulsivity. Mindfulness, 2(4), 228-235.

      Feldman, G., Lavallee, J., Gildawie, K., & Greeson, J. (2016). Dispositional Mindfulness Uncouples Physiological and Emotional Reactivity to a Laboratory Stressor and Emotional Reactivity to Executive Functioning Lapses in Daily Life. Mindfulness, 7(2), 527-541.

268   Frank, P., Stanszus, L., Fischer, D., Grossman, P., & Schrader, U. (2021, under review). What happens when people start to meditate on consumption? An explorative study inquiring into the potential of mindfulness practice for environmental and sustainability education. Journal of Environmental Education.

        Frank, P., Sundermann, A., & Fischer, D. (2019). How mindfulness training cultivates introspection and competence development for sustainable consumption. International Journal of Sustainability in Higher Education, 20(6), 1002–Geiger, S. M., & Keller, J. (2018). Shopping for Clothes and Sensitivity to the Suffering of Others: The Role of Compassion and Values in Sustainable Fashion Consumption: The Role of Compassion and Values in Sustainable Fashion Consumption. Environment and Behavior, 50(10), 1119–1144. https://doi.org/10.1177/0013916517732109

269   Donald, J., Bradshaw, E., Ryan, R., Basarkod, G., Ciarrochi, J., Duineveld, J., Guo, J., & Sahdra, B. (2020). Mindfulness and Its Association With Varied Types of Motivation: A Systematic Review and Meta-Analysis Using Self-Determination Theory. Personality and Social Psychology Bulletin, 46(7), 1121-1138.

270   A-tjak, J. G., Davis, M. L., Morina, N., Powers, M. B., Smits, J. A., & Emmelkamp, P. M. (2015). A meta-analysis of the efficacy of acceptance and commitment therapy for clinically relevant mental and physical health problems. Psychotherapy and Psychosomatics, 84(1), 30-36.

271   Fischer, D., Stanszus, L., Geiger, S., Grossman, P., & Schrader, U. (2017). Mindfulness and Sustainable Consumption: A Systematic Literature Review of Research Approaches and Findings. Journal of Cleaner Production, 162, 544–558. https://doi.org/10.1016/j.jclepro.2017.06.007

272   Ramstetter, L., Rupprecht, S., Mundaca, L., Klackl, J., Osika, W., Stenfors, C., Wamsler, C. (2022) Fostering (collective) climate action and leadership: Insights from a pilot experiment with a 10-week behavioral intervention involving mindfulness and compassion. (forthcoming).

Printed in the USA
CPSIA information can be obtained
at www.ICGtesting.com
LVHW061350130224
771619LV00040B/707